Paintings from the Muslim Courts of India

An exhibition held in the Prints and Drawings Gallery, British Museum
13 April to 11 July 1976

World of Islam Festival Publishing Company Ltd

First published 1976
ISBN 0 905035 09 7 cased
ISBN 0 905035 10 0 paper

Published and produced by the World of Islam Festival Publishing Company Ltd.

Designed by Colin Larkin
Edited by Vivienne Menkes
Set in 10/12pt Monophoto Plantin 110
Printed on 115 gsm Blade coated cartridge

Colour origination: Westerham Press
Filmset by Westerham Press and printed in England by Westerham Press Ltd., Westerham, Kent

Front cover: detail from a painting by Manōhar of Jahāngīr in private audience with Prince Khusrau. *c.* 1605–6 (109).

Back cover: prisoners of war brought before Akbar, by Ḥusayn Naqqāsh, faces by Kēsū. Right-hand page of double miniature from Ms. of *Akbarnāma*. *c.* 1590 (46).

Contents

Transliteration Note

The transliteration of Arabic and Persian is that of the modified system of the Royal Asiatic Society. The following Arabic letters, however, are transliterated according to Persian pronunciation:

ث S
ض Z
و V

As far as possible the names of Hindu artists have been given according to their transliteration in the Persian characters.

Foreword and Acknowledgements

In the winter of 1961–2 the museum presented an exhibition, 'Islamic Art in India of the Sixteenth and Seventeenth centuries'. Since then appreciation of Muslim painting of the Indian subcontinent has continued to grow; important new collections have been formed; rediscovered paintings have shed new light on the development of the various schools.

The present exhibition is intended to show the achievement of painting at the court of the Great Moghul during its greatest splendour and at the Muslim courts of the Deccan in the same period. We have drawn largely on collections in the United Kingdom which are still of prime importance. Interest in Mughal painting had been aroused in Britain long before the political connection between Britain and the subcontinent was established. Sir Thomas Roe, the accredited envoy of James I to Jahāngīr, received a signed portrait of the emperor by the artist Manōhar, which was to appear as an engraving in the published narrative of the embassy; and in 1638 the Emperor Shāh Jahān sent Charles I an illustrated manuscript of Sa'dī's *Gulistān*. Serious collecting began in the eighteenth century, with pro-consuls and statesmen, such as Clive and Warren Hastings, and servants of the East India Company, in particular Richard Johnson. Certain paintings in an album assembled in India in the seventeenth century and now in the British Museum were greatly admired by Sir Joshua Reynolds: one of these – a portrait head and shoulders – is here exhibited (**157**). In the nineteenth century, collectors were becoming increasingly numerous and by their generous gifts and legacies enriched Britain's public collections.

The Trustees wish to express their thanks to Her Majesty the Queen for graciously consenting to lend two manuscripts from the Royal Library. They also thank all those who have so generously contributed loans: the British Library Board; the Director of the Victoria and Albert Museum; the Director of the India Office Library and Records; the Curators of the Bodleian Library; the Visitors of the Ashmolean Museum;

the Director of the Fogg Art Museum, Harvard University; the Council of the Royal Asiatic Society of Great Britain and Ireland; Mr Edwin Binney; the Marquess of Bute; Mr Toby Falk; Mr Sven Gahlin; Monsieur Jean Soustiel and others who wish to remain anonymous.

They would also like to thank the World of Islam Festival Trust for a generous contribution towards the cost of the exhibition.

Thanks are also due to: Sir Robin Mackworth-Young, Her Majesty's Librarian at Windsor; Dr G. Marrison, Keeper, Mr J. Losty and Mr Q. M. Haq, Assistant Keepers, Department of Oriental Manuscripts and Printed Books, the British Library; Mr Robert Skelton, Deputy Keeper, and Miss Helen Angus, the Indian Section, the Victoria and Albert Museum; Mrs Pauline Rohatgi of the India Office Library; Mr N. C. Sainsbury, Keeper of Oriental Books, the Bodleian Library; Mr S. C. Welch of the Fogg Art Museum; Mr David Matthews of the School of Oriental and African Studies; Mr B. W. Robinson; Dr I. H. Siddiqi of the Muslim University, Aligarh; Mr Masood Abbas; and to many others on whom we have called for advice.

The selection has been made and the catalogue compiled by myself with the valuable assistance of Miss Ellen Smart and Mr Douglas Barrett, Keeper of the Department of Oriental Antiquities.

R. H. Pinder-Wilson
31 December 1975

Genealogy of the Mughal Emperors 1526–1658

Bābur (b. 1483, reigned 1526-1530)

Humāyūn (b. 1508, reigned 1530-1556)

Akbar (b. 1542, reigned 1556-1605)

Jahāngīr (Salīm) (b. 1569, reigned 1605-1627)

Murād (1570-1599)

Dānyāl (1572-1604)

Khusrau (1586-1621)

Parvīz (1589-1625)

Shāh Jahān (Khurram) (b. 1591, reigned 1628-1658, d. 1666)

Shāhryār (d. 1627)

Jahānārā Begam (1614-1681)

Dārā Shikōh (1615-1658)

Shujā‘ (1616-1659)

Aurangzīb (b. 1618, reigned 1659-1707)

Murād Bakhsh (1624-1661)

Intermarriage with family of

I‘timād al-Daula

Nūr Jahān (d. 1645)
=1. Shēr Afgan =2. **Jahāngīr** (1611)

Āṣaf Khān (1579-1641)

Lādlī Begam
=Shāhryār

Mumtāz Maḥall (d. 1631)
= **Shāh Jahān** (1612)

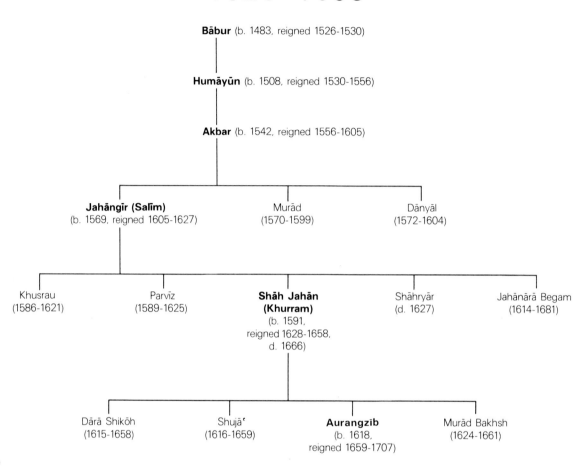

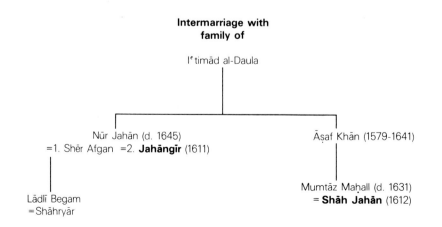

R. Oxus
Samarqand
FERGHANA
HINDU KUSH
R. Kabul
Herat
Kabul
Jalalabad
KASHMIR
Qandahar
Lahore
PUNJAB
HIMALAYAS
R. Brahmaputra
Panipat
Delhi
Pattan
R. Indus
RAJPUTANA
Amber
Agra
Jaipur
Fatehpur Sikri
Jaunpur
R. Ganges
Ajmer
R. Jumna
Allahabad
Ranthambhor
Gwalior
Chitor
MEWAR
MALWA
BENGAL
GUJARAT
Manikpur
Ahmadabad
VINDHYAS
R. Narbada
Surat
Burhanpur
AHMADNAGAR
GOLCONDA
BIJAPUR
Talikota
DECCAN
R. Krishna
VIJAYANAGAR

INDIAN SUB-CONTINENT
16th–17th century

Introduction

The destiny of the Indian subcontinent has been largely decided by the course of events in the great alluvial plain of the north. Lying between the Himalayas to the north and the Vindhyas to the south, it is watered by the great river systems of the Indus in the west and the Ganges and Brahmaputra in the east. The one weak spot in its protecting barrier of mountains was in the north-west, where the passes of the Kabul river valley invited entry by the would-be invader from the highlands of Afghanistan. It was by this north-west passage that all the great invasions of India took place.

Maḥmūd of Ghazna used this route to establish a Muslim kingdom by his conquest of the Punjab in the eleventh century. Succeeding dynasties secured possession of the greater part of the northern plain, which came to be known as Hindustan. The capital of their empire was Delhi.

The invasion of India in 1398 by Tīmūr (known in the West as Tamerlane) occurred at a moment when the Delhi sultanate was weakened by internal strife. The great conqueror had no intention of remaining in India, and before returning to Samarqand he appointed governors to rule in his name. Within fifty years of his departure a member of the Lodi family, an Afghan tribe, proclaimed himself Sultan of Delhi. His empire was no more than a shadow of that of his predecessors, for already within this and the preceding centuries the northern provinces of the sultanate had become independent Muslim kingdoms, of which the principal were Malwa, Gujarat, Kashmir and Bengal.

Bābur, founder of the Mughal dynasty of India, was born in 1483. He was descended in the fifth generation from Tīmūr. His father ruled in Ferghana, one of the numerous kingdoms which had been parcelled out from the once great Timurid Empire among Tīmūr's descendants. Called on to succeed his father when only eleven years old, he was almost at once driven out of his kingdom. His capture and loss of Samarqand were but an interlude in the life of an adventurer in search of a kingdom.

But by securing the throne of Kabul in 1504 he laid the foundations of his future career. After unsuccessful attempts to recover his ancestral domains, he turned his attention to the fertile plain of Hindustan and made plans to reconquer the territories won by his great ancestor. In the last of five expeditions he defeated the armies of the Lodi Sultan at the battle of Panipat in 1526 and occupied Agra and Delhi. In the following year he defeated the forces of the Hindu confederacy led by the great Rajput ruler of Mewar, Rana Sangram Singh. These victories gave him the mastery of all the lands between the Oxus and the frontiers of Bengal and from Gwalior to the Himalayas, but his death in 1530 prevented him from transforming what was only a military occupation into a kingdom.

His achievement proclaims his military genius, resolution and command. His memoirs, which he wrote in Turki, are a frank and intimate account of his adventurous life and reveal a remarkable personality. He was a poet who achieved considerably more than a *succès d'estime* and possessed an unusually discriminating eye for painting and nature. Some of the most eloquent passages of his memoirs are devoted to descriptions of the gardens which he created in and around Kabul.

Bābur's son Humāyūn lacked the resolution and energy of his father. Faced with rebellion by the Afghan chief Shēr Shāh, he was forced to leave India and to seek asylum with the Persian shāh, leaving the rebel to be enthroned as King of Delhi. Eventually, with Persian military aid, he was able to re-establish his court at Kabul and, on the death of Shēr Shāh in 1556, to recover his father's capital cities in India. But within seven months he was dead as the result of an accidental fall, leaving his Indian inheritance to his elder son Akbar, aged thirteen, under the tutelage of the regent, Bayrām Khān.

Neither Bābur nor Humāyūn had ruled long enough to organize an efficient kingdom. Akbar was the real founder of the Mughal Empire. In his reign of nearly fifty years he succeeded in securing control of all northern India. Thanks to Bayrām Khān, the only serious rival to the throne of Hindustan – a Hindu general, Hēmū – was defeated at another battle fought at Panipat in 1556. At eighteen Akbar dismissed the regent and set out to annex all the independent kingdoms of the north. Malwa was conquered in 1561. The subjection of the Rajput kingdom of Mewar was effected by the destruction of the great strongholds of Chitor and Ranthambhor in 1568. The conquest of Gujarat, which opened with the occupation of Surat, was completed in 1573; those of Bengal and of Kashmir were completed in 1576 and 1586.

When he was not campaigning, he resided in his principal cities, Delhi, Agra and Lahore. In 1569 he founded a new city, Fatehpur Sikri, thirty-seven kilometres west of Agra, where the Muslim saint Shaykh Salīm Chishtī had lived, and where Akbar's three sons were born. This became the capital of the empire from 1570 to 1585.

Akbar's success as a ruler was due largely to his reconciling the vast majority of his subjects who were non-Muslims by his policy of toleration. The poll tax on non-Muslims (the *jizya*) was abolished and Akbar recruited to his service Hindu generals such as Raja Man Singh, and able administrators, such as Raja Todar Mall, who reorganized the revenue system of the empire. He married Hindu wives; and the mother of his three sons was a Rajput princess, the daughter of the Raja of Amber. He even abandoned Islam and in 1582 invented and promulgated a new religion, the Divine Faith (*Dīn Ilāhī*), combining what he thought to be the best in Hinduism and Islam and designed to elevate the emperor's role as God's vicegerent. His interest in religious discussion led him to invite Jesuits from Goa to his court. The first Jesuit mission arrived in 1580, a second in 1590 and a third in 1595. Among Akbar's advisers and intimates was the historian Abu'l-Fazl. He was a mystic and visionary and was foremost in encouraging Akbar's policy of religious toleration. His chronicle of Akbar's reign (the *Akbarnāma*) is a primary source: the third part, the Institutes of Akbar (*Ā'īn-i Akbarī*) contains a survey of the empire.

The closing years of his reign were clouded by the death of his two younger sons and by the rebellion of his eldest son, Salīm, who set up his own court at Allahabad and even styled himself emperor. Father and son were reconciled, however, before Akbar died in 1605.

Prince Salīm succeeded his father under the title Jahāngīr. Like his great-grandfather he, too, wrote his memoirs (*Tūzuk-i Jahāngīrī*), in which he gives an intimate account of his court, his nobles and the great events of his reign. His relations with his own sons were not happy. His eldest son, Khusrau, rebelled against him in the second year of his reign; his third son, Khurram, was in open revolt from 1622 to 1625.

His military campaigns were principally directed to the conquest of the Deccan, which had also been a preoccupation of Akbar in the later years of his reign. The Deccan plateau forms the northern part of peninsular India and is bounded to the north by the River Narbada, and to the south by two rivers, the Krishna and the Tungabhadra. Once a province of the Delhi sultanate, it had achieved independence under the Bahmani sultans. In the late fifteenth and early sixteenth centuries it had split into five separate Muslim kingdoms, of which the three principal were Ahmadnagar under the Niẓām Shāhī kings, Golconda under the Quṭb Shāhs and Bijapur under the 'Ādil Shāhs. These kingdoms were constantly at war with one another, but in 1565 they combined to destroy the once powerful Hindu kingdom of Vijayanagar to the south, at the battle of Talikota.

Akbar had already conquered two of the smaller kingdoms of the Deccan and a part of Ahmadnagar. Jahāngīr's campaigns produced no decisive results and it was left to his successors to pursue the conquest in earnest.

Another preoccupation of Jahāngīr was his relations with Persia. Shāh 'Abbās I had tried unsuccessfully to recapture the town of Qandahar from the Mughals in 1607. Embassies between the two courts were exchanged, but when diplomacy failed the Persians resorted once again to force and captured the city in 1622.

The European powers – Portugal, Holland and England – began to figure prominently in the reign of Jahāngīr, each anxious to secure trading rights. Sir Thomas Roe, James I's accredited ambassador to Jahāngīr, reached the Mughal court in 1615 and returned home in 1619, having secured concessions which were the foundation of the East India Company's trade.

Jahāngīr died in 1627 and his son Prince Khurram was proclaimed emperor under the title Shāh Jahān at Agra in the following year. In the Deccan the kingdom of Ahmadnagar was subjugated in 1633; and the war against Bijapur and Golconda was conducted by Shāh Jahān's third son and successor, Aurangzīb. But the two kingdoms were not finally conquered until 1687, in the reign of Aurangzīb himself.

It is the person of the emperor which dominates the reign. Shāh Jahān is the 'Great Moghul' whose wealth and splendour were a legend in contemporary Europe. The foundations of the central administration of the empire were already established under Akbar. The great *durbar* scenes of Jahāngīr and Shāh Jahān catch the solemnity of these occasions. The prime minister (*vakīl*), the minister in charge of revenue and finance (*dīvān-i kull*) and the minister in charge of the army (*mīr bakhshī*) were the principal functionaries. Honorary titles such as *Khān-i Khanān* and *I'timād al-Daula* were conferred on the great dignitaries. The title of Āṣaf Khān was conferred on Abu'l-Ḥasan, son of I'timad al-Daula. His sister Nūr Jahān was married to Jahāngīr and his daughter, Mumtāz Maḥall, became the favourite wife of Shāh Jahān. He served as prime minister in the last year of Jahāngīr's reign and retained the office during the first fifteen years of the reign of Shāh Jahān.

The closing years of Shāh Jahān's reign were taken up by a bitter contest between the emperor's sons for the succession. It was finally secured by Aurangzīb, the ablest and most ruthless of the four brothers. Shāh Jahān, held captive in the fort at Agra, was deposed and Aurangzīb was enthroned at Delhi in 1659.

Paintings from the Mughal Court

Mughal painting was due to the response of the artist to one remarkable patron, the emperor Akbar; for it was his conception of the function of painting which determined the development of the school. Although his grandfather, Bābur, professed a keen appreciation of painting, there is no evidence that he was a patron of painters either in Kabul or in India. Humāyūn was the first of the Mughal emperors to establish his own studio. During his years of exile at the court of the Persian shah, he had come to know and admire the works of the Safavid court-painters at Tabriz. As soon as he was re-established in Kabul, he recruited to his service Mīr Sayyid 'Alī, an artist who already had an established reputation at the Persian court. In 1549, another Persian painter, 'Abd al-Ṣamad, also trained at Tabriz, joined Humāyūn's entourage. The painting of a young scholar (**2**) is the work of Mīr Sayyid 'Alī during these years at Kabul and is in the contemporary Safavid idiom. Another example of his work completed at this time may be the large painting on cloth of Humāyūn with his ancestor Tīmūr and relations (**1**). Apart from the figures of Akbar, Jahāngīr, Khurram, Parvīz and another standing figure which were all added about 1622, the painting is in the style of Mīr Sayyid 'Alī's Tabriz period. The only distinguishing features are the costume and peaked turban affected by the Timurid princes of Transoxiana.

Akbar as a boy had received lessons in drawing from 'Abd al-Ṣamad and had inherited his family's predilection for painting. He was only thirteen when he succeeded his father; and it was probably not before he rid himself of the tutelage of Bayrām Khān that he was able to turn his attention to his father's studio. Muslim and Hindu artists were recruited from all parts of Hindustan and were trained under the care of Mīr Sayyid 'Alī, who directed the studio until 1574, when he left India and was replaced by 'Abd al-Ṣamad. The study, and probably the copying, of the classical Persian miniatures which we know to have been in the imperial library would have formed an important part of this training. It was through this that the Mughal painters adopted many of the conventions of the Persian miniaturist, adapting them, however, to their own requirements. Many of the artists recruited were, of course, already trained in traditions of painting other than Persian. Artists from Malwa would have brought with them a style of painting which combined the idiom of Shiraz with purely indigenous elements and of which there are examples dating from the early sixteenth century. The imperial studio may, too, have attracted artists from the Muslim courts of the Deccan – Ahmadnagar, Bijapur and Golconda – of which the surviving works, it is true, are not older than the earliest Mughal paintings; but their style is distinctive enough for us to assume that it was already formed by the middle of the sixteenth century. Hindu artists would have been recruited from centres in Malwa, Gujarat and Rajputana, where they worked in the various styles which had developed out of the school of western Indian painting – the only classical school of India to survive the Muslim conquests. An unchanging feature of the school was a predilection for rendering figures in full profile.

The early stages in the growth of the Mughal style can be traced in the first great enterprise of the imperial studio. This was an illustrated copy of the *Hamzanāma*, a Persian romance dedicated to the exploits, many of them fabulous, of the Prophet's uncle Hamza, who met a hero's end at the battle of Uḥud, fighting under Muḥammad's banner. According to contemporary accounts the work comprised fourteen volumes, each containing a hundred illustrations. Each page, measuring about 45 inches square, makes this the largest of any known Mughal manuscript. With few exceptions, each illustration occupies one whole page and is painted on linen with a paper backing. The reverse contains the Persian text written on paper and attached to the backing. It is hardly surprising that the preparation of these gigantic books, begun in 1567, took fifteen years to complete.

We may suppose from the exceptionally large scale that the paintings were intended for viewing by an assembled company, when each illustration would be turned as the reciter unfolded the tale. A procedure such as this demanded a real narrative style of painting. In order to involve his viewers in the scene or episode he was illustrating, the artist used every device to achieve verisimilitude. The painter's commitment to his subject is best shown in the scenes of violence and movement. In the scene of the giant leader of the unbelievers falling headlong down a mountain side of rocky outcrops (**8**) the sheer mass of detail renders the composition hard to grasp. But there is no denying the sense of power and horror which the painter has

12

achieved in this and other similar scenes (**12, 13**). In the quieter episodes it is the evocation of nature which is a striking feature. In depicting the plantain, the mango and other exotic trees, the painter has remained remarkably true to nature (**6, 9, 11**). In the rendering of the human figure the use of the profile view – rarely used in Persian painting – adds to verisimilitude (**10**). Another important feature of these paintings is the extended palette range: tones of green and red are introduced which are unknown in contemporary Persian painting.

The painters of the *Hamzanāma* pages relied for their effects on line and colour. Their use of perspective was empirical and often faulty; and they made little or no attempt to relate the scale of figures to distance from the eye. Shortly after the completion of the *Hamzanāma*, Akbar's artists illustrated a manuscript of the *Dārābnāma*, which recounts the exploits of the Persian hero and king, Dārāb. In one of the miniatures (**17**) the painter Basāwan, besides attempting to indicate recession by perspective, has rendered the drapery on the figure of Shāpūr by shading the folds in a naturalistic manner and he gives a remarkable frontal view of the youth leaning over the prow of the boat, using the technique of foreshortening. These 'tricks' he could have learnt only from European paintings or engravings, which would have reached Akbar's court with the arrival of the first Jesuit mission in 1580 or of earlier Portuguese diplomatic missions in the 1570s. It is no wonder that Akbar, with his predilection for naturalism in art, should have responded so enthusiastically to European painting, which he set up as a yardstick of excellence. Some years later, when he came to write the *Ā'īn-i Akbarī*, Abu'l-Fazl praises the emperor's painters, 'whose works are worthy to be placed at the side of the wonderful works of the European painters'.

Now that his artists had devised a satisfactory style in which to present narrative scenes, Akbar directed his studio to producing a remarkable series of illustrated historical works. In 1589 he commissioned 'Abd al-Raḥīm, son of Bayrām Khān and one of his principal generals, to translate into Persian the memoirs of his great-grandfather, the *Bāburnāma*. Many copies were made and a number were provided with illustrations. Miniatures from four illustrated copies have survived and paintings from three of these manuscripts are included in the exhibition. The earliest belong to a copy which was prepared while 'Abd al-Raḥīm was engaged on the translation (**21–6**). With one exception (**25**), these are paired miniatures on facing pages which form a single composition. Like many other manuscript miniatures of the period of Akbar, nearly all are inscribed in red ink in the lower margin, the inscription stating that the miniature is the work of a particular artist. In one case the inscription tells us that the miniature is the combined work of two painters (**23**), the faces being the work of Nānhā, who was noted for his portraiture.

Shortly after this, another series of miniatures was prepared for a copy of the *Bāburnāma*, now in the British Library (**28–30**). These are the largest of any illustrations to the *Bāburnāma*, slightly exceeding those of a third manuscript, now dispersed, copied in about 1593 (**27**). The subjects or episodes depicted are the same in all three manuscripts, but the artists allowed themselves a certain latitude, as may be seen by comparing no. **22** with no. **27**.

For Akbar, by far the most important work of illustration was that of Abu'l-Fazl's chronicle of his own reign, the *Akbarnāma*. Exhibited are seventeen miniatures, of which ten are paired, from a copy which is believed to have been made while Abu'l-Fazl was actually composing his chronicle (**32–48**). This may explain the extraordinary vigour and immediacy of these miniatures, which in this respect differ from those of the other source of *Akbarnāma* illustrations, possibly painted after Abu'l-Fazl's death in 1602 (**49–51**).

The earlier *Akbarnāma* paintings represent the fulfilment of the Mughal narrative style. These are vivid records of Akbar's hard-fought campaigns, of his prowess as a huntsman and a tamer of wild animals, as well as his durbars and the festive scenes occasioned by the birth of a son. His artists have mastered the problem of indicating spatial relationships and of investing the human and animal figures with life and movement.

There was one other group of paintings in which Akbar's artists successfully applied the narrative style. In order to create greater mutual understanding between Muslim and Hindu, Akbar had the great Sanskrit epic the *Mahābhāratā* translated into Persian under the title *Razmnāma*. The finished copy of this work, with 169 miniatures, was presented to Akbar in 1584. It is now in the possession of the Maharajah of Jaipur. Three miniatures from another and later copy are included in the exhibition (**61–3**). These are the work of Hindu artists, who were perhaps assigned these subjects on account of their familiarity with the epic. Finer and more imaginative in conception are the five illustrations (**55–60**) to the *Harivaṃśa*, an epic devoted to Krishna, the incarnation of the God Vishnu, and appended to the *Mahābhāratā*. These splendid pages have all the drama and movement of the early *Akbarnāma* pages, with which they must be contemporary.

36

Some of the finest paintings from Akbar's studio are illustrations to the works of Persian literature (**20, 64–74**). For the most part, these manuscripts are on a far smaller scale than the historical manuscripts and were probably intended for private delectation rather than public viewing. Many of these were copied and illustrated during the last fifteen years of Akbar's reign. The Mughal artists must have been familiar with the Persian versions of those subjects they selected for illustrations, but in their own treatment of such episodes they reveal an involvement where the Persian miniaturist generally retains a certain reserve and detachment. These small-scale miniatures demanded precision of drawing and meticulous attention to detail (**20**). A feature of these later miniatures is the introduction of tonal variation to indicate distance (**65, 67, 70**). The technique could have come only from European paintings and the most likely source would have been manuscript miniatures, perhaps those of the Flemish School of the early sixteenth century.

Among the artists of the *Akbarnāma* miniatures some are singled out as portraitists (**35, 36, 46, 49**), and a portrait-painter is seen at work in a miniature of about 1590 (**81**). According to Abu'l-Fazl, Akbar sat for his own likeness and ordered portraits to be made of all his nobles, which were then assembled in a great album. No contemporary portrait of Akbar has survived, except in the narrative paintings of the *Akbarnāma*. But there are a few rare portraits of figures standing in profile – a standard pose adopted for the Mughal portrait throughout the seventeenth century (**82, 86, 91–3**) and almost certainly derived from European originals. The convention allowed small scope for indicating character or even physiognomy. Quite exceptional, however, is the portrait of the *vina*-player (**85**), in which the artist has brought his subject to life by his deft manipulation of the line.

There is good reason to believe that it was Akbar himself who directed his painters to the creation of a narrative style of painting. If, as has generally been asserted, he was unable to read, he none the less responded keenly to romance and history and to their visual realization. Abu'l-Fazl tells us how the works of his artists were shown weekly to the emperor, who conferred rewards on the deserving. We know, too, that artists sometimes accompanied the emperor on his campaigns so that they might subsequently record what they had seen; and there can be no doubt that those who painted the great scenes of the sieges of Chitor and Ranthambhor (**40, 42**) were eye-witnesses.

Jahāngīr inherited his father's taste for painting and like Bābur had an intense and sometimes morbid curiosity about nature. During the years of his open rebellion against his father he assembled round him a group of painters among whom the foremost was Āqā Rizā. This painter, originally from Herat, introduced the style current in Safavid Persia to Jahāngīr's studio (**77**). But the desire for naturalism was as strong in Jahāngīr as in his father; and this revived Persian element was absorbed into the court style of the Jahāngīr period, of which Āqā Rizā's son Abu'l-Ḥasan was a leading exponent.

Jahāngīr also shared Akbar's enthusiasm for European painting. Sir Thomas Roe relates how Jahāngīr claimed that it was impossible to distinguish between his artists' copies and the European originals (**88, 94, 121**). Nevertheless, the narrative painting of his father's studio had little or no appeal for him. The illustrations to his memoirs (*Tūzuk-i Jahāngīrī*) were painted by the leading artists of his court (**109, 111–14**). For the most part these paintings are records of particular durbars or of less formal royal occasions in which the sovereign and his sons and the great officers of state are portrayed in frozen attitudes in the performance of a ponderous court etiquette. The abandonment of the narrative style was largely due to a change in taste. The illustrated manuscript, whether literary or historical, was being displaced by the album, a collection of heterogeneous paintings and specimens of calligraphy mounted on alternate pages. The album painting was intended to be perused and enjoyed for its own sake. Typical of such paintings are the portraits of the period.

The highly finished portrait of Shāh Jahān made before he succeeded to the throne depends for its effect on the sumptuous attire and jewels (**117**). The portrait of Shāh 'Abbās (**115**) was made expressly for Jahāngīr by the artist Bishndās, who accompanied a Mughal diplomatic mission to the Persian court, in order that the emperor might have an idea of the great ruler he never met.

Among the paintings which had a particular appeal for Jahāngīr were those of what we might broadly call scientific interest. In his memoirs he has many references to the birds and animals which aroused his curiosity in the course of his travels and which his artists were required to paint. Many of these carefully observed studies (**97–9**) can stand comparison with their European counterparts, which indeed may have been their source of inspiration. One of the most remarkable paintings commissioned by Jahāngīr is that of the dying 'Ināyat Khān (**125**). He relates with characteristic detachment how he had the dying man brought into his presence in order that his artist might record the death agony of an opium-addict.

Another result of the preference for the album was the growth of *genre* painting. The rustic scene of a hunter catching squirrels in a plane tree is rendered with consummate artistry (**100**). A favourite subject, which retained its popularity throughout the seventeenth century, was religious ascetics seated in attitudes of contemplation or in conversation (**132**).

Court-painting in the reign of Shāh Jahān is directed to the glorification of the emperor. In his formal portraits Shāh Jahān is portrayed in gorgeous attire, the nimbus about his head (**136, 165**). The Great Moghul's court is revealed in all its splendour in the great double miniature from a manuscript of the *Shāhjahānnāma* (**167**). The royal house and its illustrious ancestor are commemorated in a painting of Tīmūr with the first four Mughal emperors (**138**). The equestrian portrait also enters the repertory of royal portraiture (**139, 141**). The great general and statesman Āṣaf Khān is portrayed as commander-in-chief, his troops drawn up in the background and angels overhead extolling him (**152**). Among the many portraits of the period, those rendered in line and lightly tinted have an unexpectedly intimate and personal character. The technical attainment of Shāh Jahān's artists can be seen in a group of striking *genre* scenes in which the subtle rendering of light, learned from European painting, imparts a poetic quality absent from the highly finished treatment of the royal portraits (**146, 149, 164**).

In these pages we have tried to indicate how Akbar, Jahāngīr and Shāh Jahān variously impressed their personalities on the work of their studio. We have said little about the artists themselves who were so quick to respond to their patron's intention. The work of some forty named artists is exhibited, representing but a fraction of the number of known painters at the Mughal court. Of our forty odd artists, the Hindu far outnumber the Muslim. Differences of creed, however, were submerged in the shared respect for the person of the emperor whom they were required to memorialize in their paintings.

None of the painters of the *Hamzanāma* pages is named; and apart from the guiding hands of Mīr Sayyid 'Alī and 'Abd al-Ṣamad the crucial artistic personalities in the formative period of the style elude us. There is one painter, however, who we believe cannot have failed to participate in that great enterprise. Among the artists whom Abu'l-Fazl singles out for praise is Basāwan. His known *oeuvre* is enough to establish him as an artist of far more than mere talent. His sheer range of expression puts him in a class apart. His earliest recorded work, the island scene from the *Dārābnāma* (**17**) has already been noted. Two pages which he drew for the *Akbarnāma* prove his complete mastery of the narrative style. Seldom has the miniaturist achieved such suspense and excitement as in the scene of the tiger hunt (**35**) and that of the enraged elephants (**37**). His scene of an *alfresco* feast in a woodland setting evokes a mood of pure delight and pleasure (**67**). In his later work, his tones became softer but his line no less sure. His masterpiece is an illustration to Jami's little moral tale in the *Bahāristān*, a conversation piece which expresses so deftly the discomfiture of the dervish (**70**).

1

1
The emperors and princes of the House of Tīmūr
Painting on cotton
c. 1550–60
British Museum, 1913 2–8 1, presented by the National Art Collections Fund with a contribution by W. Graham Robertson
Height (max.) 108.5 × 108cm

The painting, of which the right-hand corner and a large portion of the lower part are missing, is framed by a band of floral scrolls. The scene is a feast in a flowering meadow.

The emperors and princes descended from Tīmūr are seated in a half-circle before an octagonal pavilion: to the left, the ancestors of the Mughals, beginning with Tīmūr's third son Mīrān Shāh, Sulṭān Muḥammad, Sulṭān Abū Sa'īd, 'Umar Shaykh, Bābur, Humāyūn and his brother Kāmrān: to the right, beginning with Abū Bakr and Baysunghur and their father Shāh Rukh, Tīmūr's fourth son.

Of the four figures in the pavilion, only that on the right is contemporary with the painting. We believe this to be Tīmūr. Those of Akbar, Jahāngīr and Shāh Jahān were probably inserted in about 1622, as were the two figures standing to the left and right outside the pavilion – Jahāngīr's second son Parvīz and possibly Khusrau. The superscriptions above some of the figures were probably added at this time.

Behind the head of Akbar is the shadowy outline of a *kulāh* turban of the type worn by the Timurid emperors and princes in the painting. The erased figure was probably that of Humāyūn. Binyon (1930), however, thought it to be that of Tīmūr, since he took the right-hand figure to be Humāyūn. But it is unlikely that Jahāngīr's artist would have substituted Tīmūr for Akbar, thereby depriving the subject of its *raison d'être*. It can also be argued that the erased figure was that of Akbar himself, and that the substitution of the later portrait was necessary in order to represent Akbar as father and grandfather.

Some of the faces of the servants and pages have been restored, probably in the nineteenth century.

Published:
1921 Binyon and Arnold pl. XIII
1924 Brown pp. 149–50
1929 Stchoukine pl. III, IV
1930 Binyon
1963 Barrett and Gray p. 77f

2
A youthful scholar
By Mīr Sayyid 'Alī
c. 1550
Collection of Edwin Binney
31.8 × 20cm

The inscription in the lower part of the writing tablet (*takhta*) can be translated: 'Painted by Sayyid 'Alī, Nādir al-Mulk (servant of) Humāyūn Shāh.' Mīr Sayyid 'Alī was granted the title Nādir al-Mulk as a recompense both for his painting and his poetry; see Blochman (1965), p. 660. His pen name as a poet was Judā'ī and the verse at the top of the tablet is his.

Published:
1973 Binney no. 10
1973 Welch no. 52

3
The Qāzī who loved the farrier's daughter
By Shaḥm
Miniature (folio 91 recto) in a manuscript of Sa'dī's *Gulistān* copied by Mīr 'Alī al-Ḥusaynī at Bukhārā in 975/1567–8
1567–8
British Library, Or. 5302
27.4 × 16.9cm

The inscription on the cornice of the pavilion is a dedication to Abu'l-Ghāzī Jalāl al-Dīn Muḥammad Akbar Pādshāh.

The manuscript contains thirteen miniatures, of which six are contemporary with the manuscript and seven were added by Mughal artists in about 1605. Of the six original miniatures, this and another (folio 30 recto) contain architectural inscriptions with the dedication to Akbar.

While costume details are Mughal of the early years of Akbar's reign, the palette is that of Bukhārā. Shaḥm's signature appears on four of the miniatures.

4

a. The parrot narrates the stories to the girl
b. An exchange of words between the girl and some men
c. A jackal having turned blue is deposed as leader
d. A houseboat in a storm

Four miniatures from a manuscript of the *Tūtīnāma*
c. 1565–70
Collection of Edwin Binney
Each miniature 20.2 × 13.5cm

Published:
1973 Binney no. 12A-D
1973 Welch pp. 92–3 (reproduces c and d, the latter in colour)

5

The fairies call on Hamza to kill the dragon

Painted on cotton
Painting from the *Hamzanāma*
1567–82
Victoria and Albert Museum, I.S. 1505–1883
71.5 × 55.3cm

Published:
1925 Glück p. 34 fig. 8

4d

5

6

7

6
Rustam and Mihrafrūz converse in a garden pavilion
Painted on cotton
Painting from the *Hamzanāma*
1567–82
Victoria and Albert Museum, I.S. 1506–1883
69 × 57cm

Published:
1925 Glück p. 46 fig. 18
1921 Clarke pl. 5

7
Mihrafrūz prepares the wedding feast for Rustam
Painted on cotton
Painting from the *Hamzanāma*
1567–82
Victoria and Albert Museum, I.S. 1519–1883
69 × 57cm

Published:
1925 Glück p. 49 fig. 21
1921 Clarke pl. 6

8
Hāshim and Hāris come as veiled knights and rid Hamza's camp of the unbelievers
Painted on cotton
Painting from the *Hamzanāma*
1567–82
Victoria and Albert Museum, I.S. 1511–1883
68.9 × 52cm

Published:
1925 Glück p. 51 fig. 23
1921 Clarke pl. 10

9
'Ankārūt tempts Īrāj in the mango tree
Painted on cotton
Painting from the *Hamzanāma*
1567–82
Victoria and Albert Museum, I.S. 1512–1883
67.3 × 51.5cm

Published:
1921 Binyon and Arnold pl. II.
1921 Clarke pl. 4
1925 Glück p. 102 fig. 40

10
Mihrdukht shoots her bow at the ring
Painted on cotton
Painting from the *Hamzanāma*
1567–82
Private collection
67.5 × 52.6cm

Published:
1925 Glück p. 93 fig. 37
1963 Barrett and Gray p. 76 (in colour)

11

11
The prophet Elias rescues Prince Nūr al-Dahr from the sea into which he had been thrown by a Dīv
Painted on cotton
Painting from the *Hamzanāma*
1567–82
British Museum, 1925 9–29 02, given by the Rev. Straton Campbell
68.5 × 52cm

Published:
1928 Arnold frontispiece (in colour)
1929 Stchoukine pl. VI

12
Zumurrud Shāh falls from his castle into the court below, where he is seized by Malik Īrāj
Painted on cotton
Painting from the *Hamzanāma*
1567–82
British Museum, 1925 9–29 02, given by the Rev. Straton Campbell
68.3 × 52.5cm

13
Gardeners beating Zumurrud Shāh, who has fallen into a well
Painting from the *Hamzanāma*
1567–82
Victoria and Albert Museum, I.S. 1516–1883
67.5 × 51cm

Published:
1921 Clarke pl. 12
1925 Glück p. 104 fig. 42

14
A drunken feast
Painted on cotton
Painting from the *Hamzanāma*
1567–82
British Museum, 1948 10–9 065, given by P. C. Manuk and Miss G. M. Coles through the National Art Collections Fund
68 × 52cm

15
A cow with her calf
c. 1570
Private collection
28.3 × 18.3cm

Published:
1973 Welch no. 55

16
Portrait of Manōhar and the calligrapher Ḥusayn Zarīn Qalam
By Manōhar
1581
End-piece miniature in a manuscript of Sa'dī's *Gulistān*, copied at Fatehpur Sikri in 990/1581 by Muḥammad Ḥusayn al-Kashmīrī
Royal Asiatic Society, catalogue no. 258
Size of page within margins 32.3 × 21cm

Inscribed on the paper held by the youth: '*amal-i* [work of] *Manōhar walad-i* [son of]

Basāwan', and on that held by the figure on the right: '*Allah akbar ṣūrat-i shabīh-i Ḥusayn Zarīn Qalam*' ('God is greatest: picture of the likeness of Ḥusayn Zarīn Qalam'). The youthful painter would appear to be about fifteen years of age.

Daulat executed a portrait of him in about 1605–9. This shows the features of a man of about forty (see Godard (1936), p. 20, fig. 12). Muḥammad Ḥusayn al-Kashmīrī, given the title of Zarīn Qalam ('Golden Pen'), died in 1020/1611–12. He is the scribe of nos. 49 and 70.

Published:
1950 Ashton p. 00, no. 642, pl. 121

17
a. Dārāb receives the Ethiopians
By Narāyan
b. Tamarusia and Shāpūr reach the island of Nigar, ruled by Kharikus
By Basāwan
Miniatures (folios 33 verso and 34 recto) in a manuscript of the *Dārābnāma* by Abū Ṭāḥir ibn Ḥasan ibn 'Alī ibn Mūsā al-Tarasūsī copied in *nasta'līq*
c. 1585
British Library, Or. 4615
29 × 19cm (size of page 35.3 × 23cm)

In **a** the dress of the Ethiopians is that of the Deccan and rendered in the Deccani manner. Basāwan's beautiful painting shows his dependence on European models in certain details such as the foreshortening of the figure in the lower left leaning out of the vessel, and the naturalistic treatment of the drapery folds of the principal figures.

The manuscript contains 155 miniatures with ascriptions to forty-four artists, including 'Abd al-Ṣamad, who as director of the imperial *atelier* has corrected one of the miniatures (folio 103 verso).

Published:
1952 Wellesz pl. 35 (left-hand miniature)
1961 Welch fig. 1

18
Young man receiving a cloak from a girl
c. 1585
British Museum, 1954 5–8 01
24.5 × 18.5cm

This is a fragmentary page from a manuscript of the *Anvār-i Suhaylī*, now in the Prince of Wales Museum, Bombay.

19
a. A man hiding in an elephant skin
b. A guest petitioning a Raja
Two miniatures from a manuscript of the *Kathā Sarit Sāgara* ('Ocean of Story')
c. 1585
Collection of Edwin Binney
14.7 × 18.8cm and 12.8 × 13cm

The *Kathā Sarit Sāgara* is a collection of Hindu fables and was among those Hindu works translated into Persian and illustrated at the order of Akbar.

Published:
1973 Binney no. 26 a and b

20
a. A picnic in a tree house
By Basāwan
b. Girls dancing before a prince
By Khēm Karan
c. Distribution of alms to the poor
By Nānhā
d. A prince hunting
12.2 × 5.8cm; 10.2 × 5.6cm; 6.9 × 4.5cm; 7.4 × 4.5cm

Four miniatures from a manuscript of the *Dīvān* of Anvārī, copied at Lahore in 1588
1588
Fogg Art Museum, Harvard University, given by John Goelet

The attributions at the foot of each miniature have been partially erased.

Published:
1964 Welch pl. 4a, 4b (colour), 4c, 4d

برف گرفته بود کسی که از راه می برامد به تشویش میگذشت
این میان را تمام در برف فرو رفته آمدیم ازین جهت در توقف فرصت کابل

22b

صبح نزدیک شده بود که از دامن کوه منار سوار آمدیم
در میان کابل و منار برف تا زان اسپ بود همه جا را

22a

21
The acclaiming of the standards
Right : by Dharmdās. *Left :* by Dēvjī Gujarātī
Double miniature from a manuscript of the *Bāburnāma*, now dispersed
1589
Right : British Museum, 1948 10–9, 071
Left : Victoria and Albert Museum, I.M. 261–1913
23.8 × 132cm and 23.7 × 133cm

This ceremony was performed annually and consisted of sprinkling the yak tails of the standards with *kumis* – fermented mare's milk – to the accompaniment of pipes and drums and the war cry.

22
a. The march to Kabul
b. Bābur and his followers before the citadel of Kabul
Double miniature from a manuscript of the *Bāburnāma*, now dispersed
1589
Victoria and Albert Museum, I.M. 263–1913 and I.M. 271–1913
26.2 × 14cm and 26.1 × 23.7cm

In 1506 Bābur was called away from Kabul to aid his Timurid relatives against the Uzbeg, Shaybānī Khān. In his absence conspirators proclaimed his cousin Mīrzā Khān, king of Kabul. Bābur returned across the snow-clad passes of the Hindu Kush to find the usurper encamped outside the city laying siege to the loyalist troops in the citadel.

23
Bābur, with his architect, plans the Bāgh-i Wafā' near Jalalabad
By Bishndās, the faces by Nānhā
Double miniature from a manuscript of the *Bāburnāma*, now dispersed
1589
Victoria and Albert Museum, I.M. 276–1913 and I.M. 276a–1913
21.9 × 14.4cm and 22.2 × 13.6cm

The scene is best described in Bābur's own words:

> 'In 1508/9 I laid out the *chārbāgh* known as the Bāgh-i Wafā' ['Garden of Fidelity'] on a rising ground, facing south. . . . There oranges, citrons and pomegranates grow in abundance. The year . . . I took Lahore [1523–4] I had plantains brought and planted there; they did well. The year before, I had had sugar cane planted there; it also did well. . . . The garden lies high, had running water close at hand and a mild winter climate. In the middle of it, a one-mill stream flows constantly past the little hill on which there are four garden plots. In the south-west part of it there is a reservoir round which are orange trees and a few pomegranates, the whole encircled by a clover meadow. This is the best part of the garden, a most beautiful sight when the oranges take colour. . . .'

(Beveridge (1922) p. 208.)

Bishndās, nephew of Nānhā subsequently achieved fame as a portrait painter and was sent by Jahāngīr in 1613 with the embassy of Khān 'Ālam to the court of Shāh 'Abbās I of Persia (see no. 115).

24
Bābur supervises work in his garden at Istalif
Right : composition by Miskīna, painting by Sānwalah. *Left :* composition by Miskīna, painting by Nand Guwāliārī
Double miniature from a manuscript of the *Bāburnāma*, now dispersed
c. 1589
Collection of M. Jean Soustiel, Paris
24.6 × 13.6cm and 24.6 × 13.6cm

The village of Istalif is situated in the foothills of the Hindu Kush, fifty-five kilometres to the north of Kabul. Bābur tells us how he purchased a great garden there:

> 'There is a pleasant halting place outside it, under great plane trees, green, shady and beautiful. A one-mill stream, having grass on

both banks, flows constantly through the middle of the garden; formerly its course was zig-zag and irregular. I had it made straight and orderly . . .'
(Beveridge (1969) p. 216.)

Published:
1973 Soustiel

24

24

26

26

25

25
A water tiger attacking a buffalo
By Bhagwān
Miniature from a manuscript of the
Bāburnāma, now dispersed
c. 1589
Victoria and Albert Museum, I.S. 234–1950 recto
19 × 10.2cm

This is an illustration to a section of the *Bāburnāma* in which Bābur describes the animals, birds and plants of Hindustan. On this page he describes the koel (*eudynamys orientalis*), the shiqarrak (the green magpie) and the water tiger (*crocodilus palustris*), 'which is like a lizard. People say it carries off men and even buffaloes'. (Beveridge (1922) p. 501.)

26
Bābur's garden party at Agra to celebrate the conquest of Hindustan
Right: Rāmdās. *Left:* by Madhū Chēla
Double miniature from a manuscript of the
Bāburnāma, now dispersed
c. 1589
Victoria and Albert Museum, I.M. 275–1913 and I.M. 274–1913
25 × 15cm and 24.2 × 13.9cm

The celebration depicted here took place at Agra in 1528. Bābur had defeated Ibrāhīm Lōdī at the battle of Panipat in 1526. Relations from Persia and Transoxiana as well as envoys from the Persian shah and the Uzbeg ruler were invited to attend. Here the guests are offering gifts to Bābur. In the meantime they were entertained by camel and elephant fights (Beveridge (1922) p. 631).

A note in the margin of the right-hand miniature states that Rāmdās worked on the painting for fifty days.

27
Bābur arrives at the camp of Mīrzā Khān
Left: half of a double miniature from a
manuscript of the *Bāburnāma*, now dispersed
c. 1593
Private collection
25.2 × 15.8cm

This miniature comes from another manuscript made some four years after the manuscript from which nos 21–6 were detached. Two leaves from this second manuscript are in the Musée Guimet, Paris, thirty-four in the Walters Art Gallery, Baltimore and fifty-nine in the State Museum of Eastern Cultures, Moscow.

The incident depicted here is that illustrated in the double miniature from the earlier *Bāburnāma* manuscripts (no. 22). In this version the artist has given greater prominence to Mīrzā Khān's camp in the garden and less to the city of Kabul.

Published:
1976 Skelton V 44

28
Bābur after his second capture of Samarqand, receives the notables of the city
Miniature detached from a manuscript of the *Bāburnāma*, now in the British Library (see no. 30)
c. 1590
Private collection
29.2 × 16.2cm

Bābur made his first capture of Samarqand in 1497 when he was only fourteen, but he held the city for only three months. In 1500 Samarqand passed into the hands of the warlike Uzbeg, Shaybānī Khān. One night in the autumn of that year, Bābur and his followers forced an entry while the Uzbegs were camped outside the city. His occupation was again brief, for Shaybānī Khān returned in the spring of 1501 and after besieging Bābur recaptured the city.

29
Bābur receives Jahāngīr Mīrzā in the ḥammām at Akhsi
Miniature detached from a manuscript of the *Bāburnāma*, now in the British Library (see no. 30)
c. 1590
Private collection
29.2 × 16.2cm

In 1502 Bābur was at Akhsī in his ancestral kingdom of Ferghana when his brother Jahāngīr Mīrzā brought him information that Tambal, a Timurid cousin, was intending to attack the city.

30
Bābur at Agra presents gifts to Humāyūn in 1526
By Bhūra
Double miniature (folios 417 verso and 418 recto) in a manuscript of the *Bāburnāma*
c. 1590
British Library, Or. 3714
28.2 × 15cm and 27.3 × 14.9cm

This copy of the *Bāburnāma* was made soon after the completion of the dispersed manuscript (nos 21–6). It originally contained 183 miniatures, but now has only 152. The 31 missing miniatures were extracted when the manuscript was still in the Royal Library in Delhi at the beginning of the nineteenth century. Of these, two are now in the Pierpont Morgan Library, New York, one in the Cleveland Museum, one in the Bibliothèque Nationale, Paris, and two in a private collection (exhibited here as nos. 28 and 29).

The miniatures in this manuscript are the largest in size of all the surviving *Bāburnāma* miniatures.

31
Bābur at Agra presents gifts to Humāyūn in 1526
Double miniature from an album
c. 1800
Victoria and Albert Museum, I.S. 127–1921 and I.S. 128–1921
28.4 × 15.6cm and 27.5 × 15.6cm

This painting was copied from a double miniature in the manuscript of the *Bāburnāma* in the British Library (no. 30) and is typical Delhi work of the early nineteenth century. It was then mounted in the so-called *Wantage Album*, now in the Victoria and Albert Museum.

Published:
1922 Clarke pl. 2

32
Muḥammad Amīn Dīvāna escorts the widow of Bayrām Khān and her son to Ahmadabad
By Makand
Miniature from a maunscript of the *Akbarnāma*
c. 1590
Victoria and Albert Museum, I.S. 2–1896 6/117
32.1 × 19cm

Bayrām Khān, the young Akbar's guardian, acted as regent until his dismissal in 1560. He was subsequently assassinated in Gujarat on his way to Mecca.

This miniature and nos 33–48 are from the manuscript of the *Akbarnāma* prepared by its author Abu'l-Fazl for Akbar and containing the history of Akbar from 1561 to 1578. This is the second of three volumes; the first and third have disappeared, although detached miniatures are known. (See Binney (1973), p. 40.)

The text of this second volume is exhibited.

33
Dancing girls and musicians performing at a marriage
Right: composition by La'l, painting by Banwālī the younger. *Left:* composition by La'l, painting by Sānwala
Double miniature from a manuscript of the *Akbarnāma*
c. 1590
Victoria and Albert Museum, I.S. 2–1896 9/117
32 × 18.9cm and 32 × 25cm

31

31

The occasion was the marriage of the son of Akbar's foster mother, Māham Anaga, in 1561. His foster mother is seated in front of the enthroned Akbar, the son immediately below his mother.

34
Dancing girls perform before Akbar
Composition by Kēsū Kahār, painting by Dharmdās
Miniature from a manuscript of the *Akbarnāma*
c. 1590
Victoria and Albert Museum, I.S. 2–1896 16/117
32.6 × 18.8cm

In the campaign against the independent province of Malwa in 1561, Akbar's general Adham Khān succeeded in capturing the harem of Bāz Bahādur, ruler of Malwa. The harem was brought to Akbar's court to perform before the emperor.

35
Akbar kills a tiger
Right : composition and faces by Basāwan, painting by Tārā the elder. *Left :* composition by Basāwan, painting by Sarwan
Double miniature from a manuscript of the *Akbarnāma*
c. 1590
Victoria and Albert Museum, I.S. 2–1896, 17 and 18/117
31.8 × 19.3cm and 3.15 × 19.3cm

Akbar killed his first tiger while hunting near Narwar, Gwalior, in 1561.

Published:
1971 Gascoigne pp. 112–13

36
Akbar visits the shrine of Mu'īn al-Dīn Chishtī
Composition by Basāwan, painting by Ikhlāṣ, faces by Nānhā
Miniature from a manuscript of the *Akbarnāma*
c. 1590
Victoria and Albert Museum, I.S. 2–1896 45/117
32.3 × 20.3cm

Akbar made his first pilgrimage to the shrine of Mu'īn al-Dīn Chishtī at Ajmer in 1562.

Published:
1952 Wellesz pl. 16

37
Akbar rides the elephant Hawā'ī
Right and left : composition by Basāwan, painting by Chitra
Double miniature from a manuscript of the *Akbarnāma*
c. 1590
Victoria and Albert Museum, I.S. 2–1896 21 and 22/117
34.5 × 21.6cm and 34.5 × 21.7cm

This well-known incident took place outside the fort of Agra. Akbar displayed his prowess by mounting an elephant notorious for its intractability and set it against another elephant equally fierce. The elephants then proceeded across the pontoon bridge over the Jumna, at great risk to Akbar. Eventually he succeeded in taming the beast.

This dramatic scene is depicted in a masterly way in the left-hand miniature. In the right-hand miniature Atga Khān, Akbar's chief minister (*vakīl*) and the court anxiously regard the contest.

Published:
1924 Brown pl. XXXIX

ان جشن دل افروز هر روز بطرزی خاص مرتب میشد و مواد بهجت و خرمی بخاص و عام مهیا میگشت

33

33

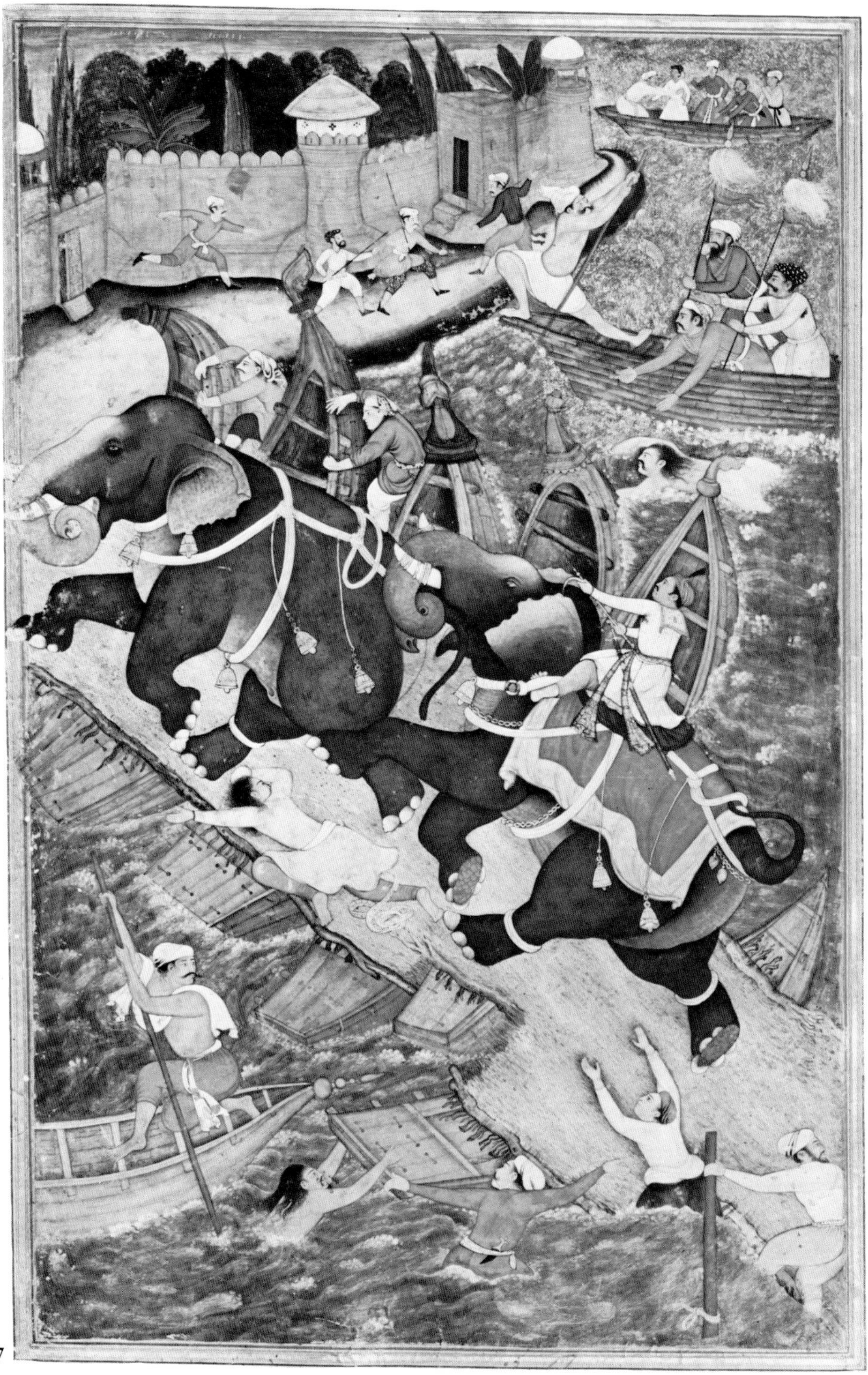

37

37

39

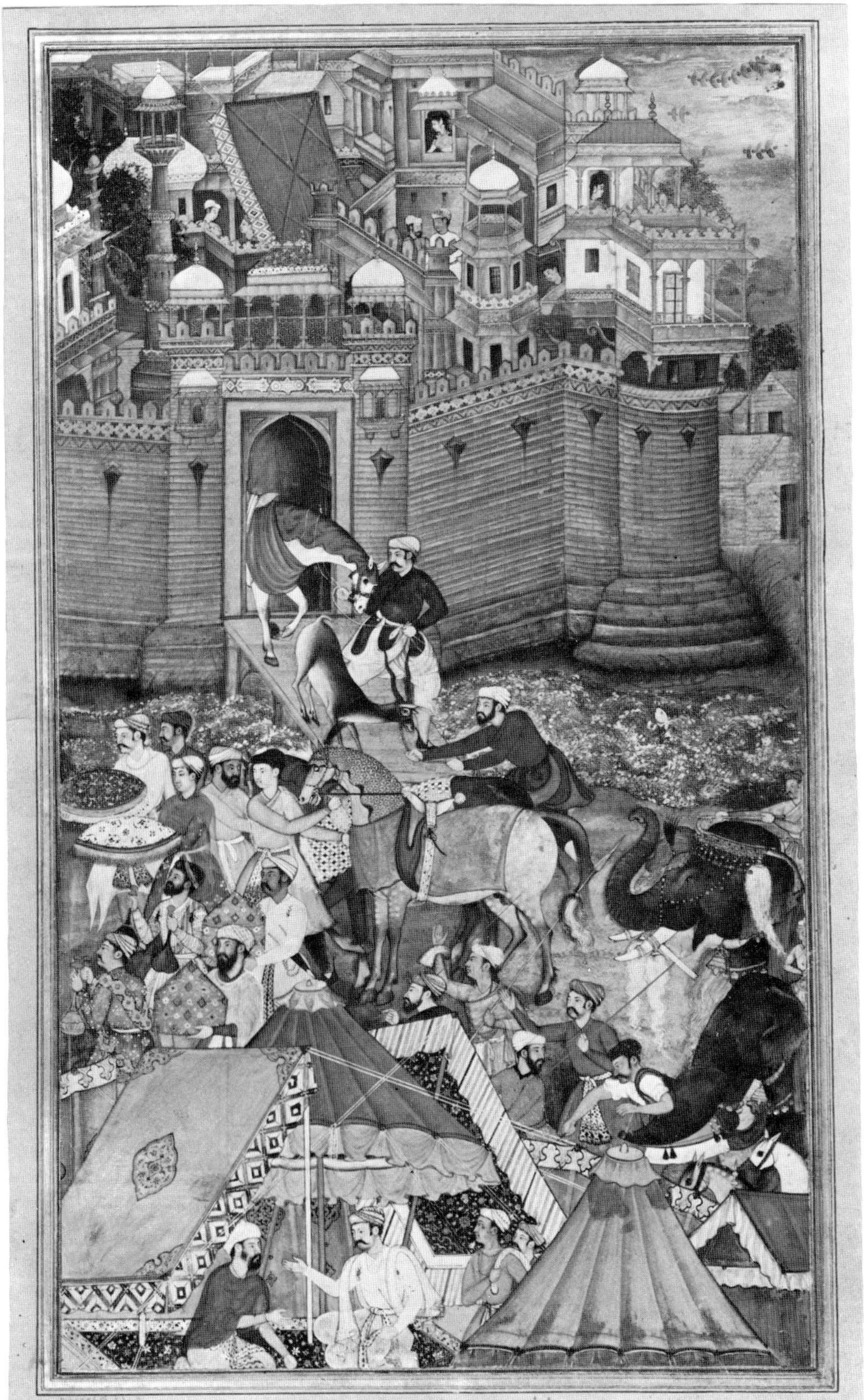

39

38
Building the Fort at Agra
Right : composition by Miskīna, painting by Sarwan. *Left :* composition by Miskīna, painting by Tulsī the younger
Double miniature from a manuscript of the *Akbarnāma*
c. 1590
Victoria and Albert Museum, I.S. 2–1896 45 and 46/117
32.7 × 19.8cm and 32.5 × 20cm

The great palace fortress of Agra – Akbar's first major architectural undertaking – was completed in 1566 under the supervision of Qāsim, the overseer of buildings and ships (*Mīr Barr u Baḥr*). Abu'l Fazl gives a vivid account of its building, work being carried out by three to four thousand builders and labourers. The enclosure wall, 21 metres high and nearly 2 kilometres in circuit, was built of dressed limestone blocks 'joined so closely that even a hair cannot find its way into their joints' (Beveridge (1902), II, pp. 372–3).

39
Akbar receives gifts while encamped near Jaunpur
Right : by Nānhā. *Left :* composition by Miskīna, painting by Bhagwān
Double miniature from a manuscript of the *Akbarnāma*
c. 1590
Victoria and Albert Museum, I.S. 2–1896 51 and 52/117
33.3 × 19.5cm and 33.8 × 19.9cm

From 1565 to 1567 Akbar was occupied in suppressing rebellion by the disaffected Uzbeg officers in his service in the eastern provinces. He himself took the field in May 1565 and succeeded in forcing the rebels to raise the siege of Manikpur. Encamped outside Jaunpur, Akbar received gifts from his generals, who joined him from Manikpur.

In the two miniatures, the Ganges flows below the walls of the city of Jaunpur. Āṣaf Khān, who had been one of the generals besieged in Manikpur, stands before the emperor offering him gifts of horses and elephants.

40
Mining operations at the siege of Chitor
Right : composition by Miskīna, painting by Sarwan. *Left :* composition by Miskīna, painting by Bhūra
Double miniature from a manuscript of the *Akbarnāma*
c. 1590
Victoria and Albert Museum, I.S. 2–1896 66 and 67/117
33 × 18.9cm and 33.1 × 19.3cm

Having failed to take the great fortress of Chitor by direct assault, Akbar decided to use mines. On 17 December 1567 two mines were fired but the storming party rushed into the breach before the second mine exploded. Of the two hundred troops killed, one hundred were officers.

This incident is depicted in the left-hand miniature. In the right-hand miniature, sappers are constructing a covered approach.

41
A mortar being dragged to the battery at the siege of Ranthambhor
Composition by Miskīna, painting by Paras
Miniature from a manuscript of the *Akbarnāma*
c. 1590
Victoria and Albert Museum. I.S. 2–1896 72/117
33.5 × 18.6cm

The fort of Ranthambhor was captured in 1569 after a siege of just under six weeks.

Published:
1929 Stchoukine pl. XI

42
The second siege of Ranthambhor
Composition by Miskīna, painting by Bhūra.
Miniature from a manuscript of the *Akbarnāma*
c. 1590
Victoria and Albert Museum, I.S. 2–1896 74/117
33 × 19.5cm

43
Akbar's entry into the fort of Ranthambhor
Composition by La'l, painting by Shankar
Miniature from a manuscript of the *Akbarnāma*
c. 1590
Victoria and Albert Museum, I.S. 2–1896 76/117
33.5 × 20.3cm

According to an inscription in the lower margin the miniature was completed in sixty-five days.

44
Rejoicings at the birth of Akbar's son, Salīm
Right: composition by Kēsū the elder, painting by Dharmdās. *Left*: composition by Kēsū the elder, painting by Chitra
Double miniature from a manuscript of the *Akbarnāma*
c. 1590
Victoria and Albert Museum. I.S. 2–1896 78 and 79/117
32.2 × 19cm and 32 × 19.1cm

Akbar's son and successor was born at Fatehpur Sikri on 30 August 1569 in the hospice of Shaykh Salīm Chishtī, a Sufi saint, much venerated by the emperor. The child received the name of Salīm in honour of the saint.

The miniature on the right shows the scene in the hospice at Sikri; that on the left, Akbar receiving congratulations at Agra.

Published:
1948 Wilkinson pl. 5

45
The battle of Pattan
Right: composition by La'l, painting by Dhasnūn. *Left*: composition by La'l, painting by Manī
Double miniature from a manuscript of the *Akbarnāma*
c. 1590
Victoria and Albert Museum, I.S. 2–1896 108 and 109/117
31.8 × 20.5cm and 32.5 × 20.7cm

This was one of the battles fought during Akbar's campaign for the conquest of Gujarat.

46
Prisoners of war brought before Akbar
Right: by Ḥusayn Naqqāsh, faces by Kesū. *Left*: composition by Basāwan, painting by Manṣūr
Double miniature from a manuscript of the *Akbarnāma*
c. 1590
Victoria and Albert Museum, I.S. 2–1896 112 and 113/117
33 × 19cm and 32 × 19.3cm

In 1572–3 Akbar's generals were occupied in expelling the rebellious *mīrzās* – princes of the Timurid house – from Gujarat. Those taken prisoner were brought to Akbar at Fatehpur Sikri, where they were subjected to the humiliation of being clothed in animal skins.

Among the courtiers and soldiers standing before Akbar on the right is a dark-skinned figure wearing a white turban. This is the *vina*-player Naubat Khān, who was greatly esteemed by Akbar and is the subject of the painting by Manṣūr (no. 85).

40

40

44

44

47
Akbar's entry into Surat
By Farrukh Beg
Miniature from a manuscript of the *Akbarnāma*
c. 1590
Victoria and Albert Museum, I.S. 2–1896
117/117
32 × 19.3cm

Akbar captured the fort at Surat early in 1573 after a brief siege.

Farrukh Beg, an artist of Persian origin, arrived at Akbar's court in 1584. His style is distinctive (see Skelton (1957) pp. 393–411).

48
Akbar orders his followers to cease the slaughter
Miniature from a manuscript of the *Akbarnāma*
c. 1590
India Office Library
30.6 × 18.5cm

At a *qamargāh* held near Bhera in 1578, Akbar underwent a sudden revulsion at the carnage.

This miniature either comes from the manuscript in the Victoria and Albert Museum which forms the second volume and breaks off in 1577 or it belongs to the missing third volume.

Published:
1950 Ashton p. 130

49
Festivities on the occasion of Akbar's circumcision
By Madhū, faces by Nar Singh
Miniature (folio 114 recto) in a manuscript of the *Akbarnāma* copied by Muḥammad Ḥusayn Kashmīrī Zarīn Qalam
c. 1600–5.
British Library, Or. 12988, the gift of P. T. Brooke-Sewell
23 × 12.3cm (including text)

The festivities were held in the Urta Garden outside Kabul in March, 1546.

This is the first of a three-volume manuscript of the *Akbarnāma*; the second and part of the third volume are in the Chester Beatty Library, Dublin. This first volume contains no colophon but a note at the foot of the miniature on folio 134 verso reads: 'In 1012, the 21st of the divine month Sha'bān in the [regnal] year 47 [by] Khēm Karan.' 21 Sha'bān 1012 A.H. corresponds to A.D. 25 January 1604; the 47th regnal year to 1010. The writer has mistakenly written 47 for 49. We may assume therefore that work on the manuscript was still in progress at the beginning of 1604. A library accession note in the hand of Jahāngīr, partially defaced, on the first folio is dated 1028/1619 and includes the words *Kashmīrī kih dar 'ilm-i khatt . . .* (Kashmīrī who in the art of writing . . .), which can refer only to Muḥammad Ḥusayn Kashmīrī.

Published:
1912 Martin pl. 183

50
Akbar on a hunting expedition
Miniature from a manuscript of the *Akbarnāma*, copied by Muḥammad Ḥusayn al-Kashmīrī Zarīn Qalam
c. 1600–5
Collection of Edwin Binney
22.7 × 12.8cm

The incident has not been identified. The miniature comes from a three-volume manuscript of the *Akbarnāma*, of which the first is in the British Library, the second and part of the third in the Chester Beatty Library, Dublin.

Published:
1973 Binney no. 20

No. 1

No. 99

آن پارچه خان بپای خود زیر کرده ایستاد و یک پارچه
دیگر را که بهمان طریق بیک توغ دیگر بسته بودند من زیر
کرده ایستادم و کنار یک پارچه دیگر را سلطان محمد خانکه ان مغولی کم
این پارچه را بسته است دست کاور ابدست خود گرفته بزبان

No. 21

ایستاده کرده یک مغول به یک دست کاو یک کرباس
سفید درازی را بسته در دست خود گرفته ایستاده است
دیگری سه پارچه سفید دراز را پایان تر از قطاس توغ
بسته و از زیر چوب توغ گذرانده و آورده یک کنار

No. 21

No. 176

No. 102

No. 64

No. 171

No. 126

No. 124

51

Humāyūn resting on a hawking expedition

Miniature from a manuscript of the *Akbarnāma* copied by Muḥammad Ḥusayn Zarīn Qalam
c. 1600–5.
India Office Library, *Johnson Album* 64, no. 37
19.5 × 11.5cm

This miniature is from the volume of the *Akbarnāma* manuscript now in the British Library (see no. 49).

52

The Caliph al-Ma'mūn receiving homage

Illustration from a manuscript now dispersed of the *Ta'rīkh-i Alfī*
c. 1593
Collection of Edwin Binney
39.4 × 22.5cm

The *Ta'rīkh-i Alfī* ('History of a Thousand Years') was compiled by order of Akbar to celebrate the millennium (in lunar years) of the Hijra (the Prophet's flight from Mecca to Medina in 622 A.D.), which was due to occur in 1592–3. The work was begun by a team of scholars under the supervision of the court historian Badā'ūnī, who in 1593 presented the three finished volumes to the emperor. Akbar himself had contributed the introduction. Abu'l-Fazl makes no mention in the *Ā'īn-i Akbarī* of an illustrated copy from which this and the following painting may have been detached. The copy may have been made when Abu'l-Fazl was making the final revision of the original, or shortly after its completion.

This and the following page, as well as other pages now in public and private collections from the dispersed manuscript, have one feature in common: the Persian text is 'suspended' in front of the scene depicted, so that the action is confined to the area between the text and ruled margins.

Published:
1973 Binney no. 16

53

Destruction of the tomb of Ḥusayn at Kerbela by order of the Abbasid caliph al-Mutawakkil

Page from a manuscript, now dispersed, of the *Ta'rīkh-i Alfī*
c. 1590
British Museum, 1934 1–13 01
40.2 × 22cm

Published:
1934 Gray pp. 149–51 pl. XLIX

53

54
Mangū Khān judges the rebels
Composition by Tulsī, painting by Paras
Miniature from a manuscript of the Jāmi'
al-Tavārīkh, copied in 1004/1596–7
Collection of Edwin Binney
37.1 × 20.8cm

The greater part of this manuscript is in the Gulistan Library, Tehran (see Hajek (1960) pp. 2–5).

Published:
1973 Binney no. 17

55

55
Krishna in combat with Indra
Miniature from a manuscript of the *Harivaṃśa*, now dispersed
c. 1590
Victoria and Albert Museum, I.S. 5–1970
29.6 × 18.2cm

Krishna rides on his eagle, Garuḍa, and attacks Indra mounted on his white elephant. Other gods watch this contest, which takes place in the sky.

Published:
1970 Skelton fig. 5

56
Krishna received by Raja Bhismaka
Miniature from a manuscript of the *Harivaṃśa*, now dispersed
c. 1590
Victoria and Albert Museum, I.S. 4–1970
32 × 19.9cm

Rukmini, the Raja's daughter, holds a garland towards Krishna, indicating that it is he whom she chooses for a husband.

Published:
1970 Skelton fig. 4

57
Krishna kills Raja Kaṃśa
Miniature from a manuscript of the *Harivaṃśa*, now dispersed
c. 1590
Victoria and Albert Museum, I.S. 3–1970
32.3 × 20.4cm

The Raja having failed to secure the death of Krishna and his brother, Balarama, is in his turn killed by the brothers. Krishna is represented as dark blue, since he was conceived from a black hair from Vishnu's head; Balarama is white, since he was conceived from a white hair.

Published:
1970 Skelton pl. 2 (colour)

58
Shiva destroys the demon Andhaka
Miniature from a manuscript of the *Harivaṃśa*, now dispersed
c. 1590
Victoria and Albert Museum, I.S. 7–1970
31.2 × 18.5cm

Shiva, decked with snake, shawl, crescent moon and necklace of skulls, rides forward on his bull Nandi to drive his flaming trident into the demon's heart.

Published:
1970 Skelton fig. 8

59

59
Krishna as a cowherd
c. 1590
British Museum, 1949 2–12 04
30 × 20.5cm

This page may come, like nos 55–60, from a manuscript of the *Harivaṃśa*, now dispersed, of which at least twenty-nine miniatures survive (see Skelton (1970) pp. 41–54).

60.
Demons preparing food by a torrent
c. 1590
Collection of Edwin Binney
21.8 × 12.2cm

This may possibly be an illustration, slightly cut down, to a manuscript of the *Harivaṃśa* (see nos 55–8). This form of demon is derived from the Safavid painting of Persia.

Published:
1973 Binney no 27

61
The second adventure of the white horse
By Banwārī the younger
Miniature (folio 26 verso) in a manuscript of the *Razmnāma* copied in 1007/1598
British Library, Or. 12076
31 × 43cm

For this manuscript, see Pinder-Wilson (1956)

62
Krishna and the Pāṇḍavas visit the dying Bhīṣma who discourses to them on the duties of kings
By Rāmdās
British Museum, 1930 7–16 01
24.5 × 14.3cm

The miniature comes from a companion volume, now dispersed, of the *Razmnāma* manuscript (for description see no. 61).

63
Yudiṣṭhhira wrestling with Karṇa
By Mākir
Illustration to the *Razmnāma*
1598
British Museum, 1921 11–15 013
20.3 × 11.5cm

The miniature comes from a companion volume, now dispersed, of the *Razmnāma* manuscript (for description see no. 61).

64
Rūdāba lets down her tresses for Zāl to climb
Miniature from a manuscript of the *Shāhnāma*
c. 1580
Private collection
25 × 15.8cm

According to Skelton (1970), p. 238, the painting comes from the royal copy of the *Shāhnāma*, which the historian Badā'ūnī tells us was in the library in 1582.

65
Right: **Majnūn in the desert**
By Dhanwān
Left: **The king of Mero throws a bound youth to the dogs**
By Āsī
Miniatures (ff. 65, 66) in a manuscript of Niẓāmī's *Laylā and Majnūn*
c. 1590
Bodleian Library, Ms. Pers. d. 102
22.4 × 16cm and 20.3 × 15.5cm

The manuscript was probably copied about the middle of the sixteenth century in Persia and the nine miniatures were added towards the end of the century in India. It belonged at one time to James Atkinson, whose English translation of Niẓāmī's *Layla and Majnūn* was published in 1836.

Published:
1952 Beeston pp. 63–6 pl. VIII
1953 *Mughal Miniatures* pl. 1

66
Shīrīn is shown the portrait of Khusrau
c. 1590–1600
Bodleian Library, Ms. Pers. b.1. folio 28 verso
27 × 20cm

This is almost certainly an illustration to Niẓāmī's *Khusrau and Shīrīn.* Shāpūr was sent by his friend Khusrau, the Persian emperor's son, to present the prince's portrait to the Armenian princess, Shīrīn. The original text has been replaced by four lines of prose describing the incident.

Shīrīn is seated in a pavilion set within an inner court of the palace. The rear wall is richly decorated with flying angels (*peris*).

Published:
1929 Stchoukine pl. VII

67
a. The arrival of a prince
By Kēsū Dās
b. The poet spurned

Attributed to Basāwan
Two miniatures from a manuscript of the *Dīvān* of Shāhī
c. 1593
Private collection
12.6 × 8.5cm and 12.7 × 8.1cm

Published:
1959 Welch figs 4, 5
1964 Welch pl. 4, 5A, 5B

68
The raven addressing the assembled animals
Late sixteenth century
British Museum, 1920 9–17 05
27 × 19.4cm

The raven stands just below the summit of the mountain: the phoenix is prominent among the birds that throng the sky. Animals are gathered on the slope of the mountain, and aquatic creatures in the water in the foreground.

68

Lines of text in the top left-hand corner have been painted all over. The manuscript from which the painting was extracted is not known. There is another version of the subject, resembling this both in composition and detail, in the Freer Gallery of Art (see Glynn (1974) p. 68, no. 4).

69
Iskandar's horse is washed in the Fountain of Life
By Kanak Singh Chēla
Miniature (folio 281 verso) in a manuscript of Niẓāmī's *Khamsa* copied by 'Abd al-Raḥīm 'Ambarīn Qalam 1004/1595–6
British Library, Or. 12208
21.8 × 13.5cm

The margins of this sumptuous manuscript are illuminated throughout. Of the original forty-four miniatures, thirty-seven are still in the book.

The work of the artist Kanak Singh is also represented in a manuscript of the *Tīmūrnāma* in the Oriental Public Library, Bankipur.

The *Iskandarnāma*, one of the five romances of Niẓāmī's *Khamsa*, relates the adventures of Alexander the Great, known in the Islamic world as Iskandar.

70
A mullā rebukes a dervish for pride
By Basāwan
Miniature (folio 9 recto) in a manuscript of Jāmī's *Bahāristān* copied at Lahore by Muḥammad Ḥusayn Zarīn Qalam in 1595
Bodleian Library, Elliot 254
21.5 × 14.6cm

Published:
1924 Brown p. XXXV
1961 Welch p. 14f and fig. 3

71
Abu'l-Adyān gives proof that fire submits to the will of God
By Daulat
Miniature (folio 135 verso) in a manuscript of Jāmī's *Nafaḥāt al-Uns* copied in *nasta'līq* by 'Abd al-Raḥīm known as 'Ambarīn Qalam for the library of Akbar, in Agra in the forty-ninth regnal year (A.D. 1603).
c. 1603
British Library, Or. 1362
25 × 13cm

Jāmī's *Nafaḥāt al-Uns* ('Breaths of Fellowship'), composed in 1476, contains the biographies of more than six hundred Sufi saints. This copy originally contained thirty miniatures. Some of the missing pages are now in the Chester Beatty Library, Dublin.

Published:
1952 Wellesz pl. 35

72
Right : **a mullā seated by a river**
By Hīranand *Left :* **prince visiting a dervish**
Miniatures (folio 74 verso and 75 recto) from a manuscript of the *Kulliyat* of Sa'dī
c. 1605
Collection of the Marquess of Bute
27.3 × 14.9cm (each miniature)

73
A hermit brings Layla to Majnūn
Miniature (folio 34 verso) in a manuscript of Niẓāmī's *Layla and Majnūn* copied by Muḥammad Bāqir ibn Mullā Mīr 'Alī in 965/1558
1605–10
India Office Library, no. 384

The five miniatures were added in the spaces left vacant by the copyist, in about 1605–10. The miniature exhibited reflects the Persian taste introduced by Āqā Rizā, in particular the figures of Layla and the hermit.

Published:
1957 Pinder-Wilson p. 414f. and fig. 3

74
Farhād beside the pool at the entrance to the tunnel which he dug through Mount Bisitūn
By Nadīm
Illustration to Niẓāmī's *Khusrau and Shīrīn*
c. 1605
British Museum, 1920 9–17 0267
16.2 × 10.8cm

Inscribed on rock at bottom right: *'amal-i Nadīm* (the work of Nadīm).

75
The hare by a ruse causes the lion to be drowned in a well
Miniature (folio 43 verso) in a manuscript of the *Anvār-i Suhaylī* by Ḥusayn Vā'iẓ al-Kāshifī, copied at Ahmadabad by Taymur Hamūs in 1009/1600–1.
British Library, Or. 6317
22.1 × 12.2cm (gold ruled text area)

This manuscript, containing forty-three miniatures, was painted in a private *atelier* at Ahmadabad.

Published:
1969 Pinder-Wilson p. 165, fig. 105

73

76

Solomon enthroned

Miniature (folio 14 recto) in a manuscript of the *Dīvān* of Hāfiẓ, copied in *nasta'līq*
c. 1600–5.
British Library, Grenville XLI
8.3 × 4.8cm

The poet alludes in the facing ode (*ghazal*) to the lover who 'is the Solomon of the time since he is Lord of the Ring'. Solomon, with his ring engraved with 'the Most Great Name' of God, ruled over birds, beasts, fishes, the winds, men and the *jinn*.

The manuscript, which has been re-marginated, contains nineteen miniatures. The fragmentary fly-leaf bears an autograph note by Shāh Jahān recording his possession of the manuscript in 1037/1625–6 and another note, possibly by Jahāngīr, stating that it entered his library in Allahabad.

74

77

The young hawk and the hunt

By Āqā Rizā
Miniature (folio 36 recto) in a manuscript of the *Anvār-i Suhaylī* by Ḥusayn Vā'iẓ al-Kāshifī copied in 1019/1610–11.
British Library, Add. 18579
17 × 9cm

Inscribed on miniature: *'amal-i Muḥammad Rizā Murīd-i Pādshāh, 1013 A.H.* (the work of Muḥammad Rizā, servant of the emperor, A.D. 1604–5).

Of the thirty-six miniatures this and another, also by Āqā Rizā, are dated six years before the completion of the manuscript and a year before Jahāngīr succeeded to the throne. Āqā Rizā, father of Abu'l-Ḥasan, was originally from Herat and joined the court of Jahāngīr, then Prince Salīm, at least as early as 1589, for, according to the inscription on no. 87, his son was born in the palace in that year.

Published:
1929 Wilkinson pl. IV

78

Illuminated borders

Manuscript of the *Dīvān* of Hāfiz copied in Persia in the first half of the sixteenth century
Late sixteenth century (margin and decorations)
Collection of the Marquess of Bute
24.5 × 18.5cm (each page)

The illuminations in the margins are executed in colour and two shades of gold.

79

A holyman

By Makand
*c.*1585
Collection of Sven Gahlin
11.3 × 5.8cm

According to the couplet inscribed at the top of the painting, the holy man belongs to the Qalandarī sect, members of which carry the horn flute depicted here.

The painting is signed by Makand, whose earliest work is in the great manuscript of the *Razmnāma*, now in Jaipur. He contributed compositions and paintings to many of the historical manuscripts and is mentioned in the *Ā'īn-i Akbarī* as one of those artists who achieved fame.

80

A European gentleman

c. 1590
Victoria and Albert Museum, I.M. 9–1913
33 × 19cm

This is related to two other paintings of Europeans, one of which is in the Victoria and Albert Museum and another is published by Martin (1912), pl. 170. All three are probably free interpretations of European engravings, probably of Dutch or Flemish origin.

81

An artist painting a portrait

c. 1590
Private collection
14.5 × 8cm

Published:
1976 Skelton V42

82

Zayn Khān Kōka

c. 1590
Victoria and Albert Museum, I.S. 91–1965
10.2 × 6.7cm

The inscription, *Zayn Khān Kōka*, is in the hand of Jahāngīr. He served in Akbar's army, mainly in the north-west, and was made governor of Kabul in 1597. In the same year his daughter was married to Prince Salīm. He died in 1600.

83

The yellow-backed woodpecker

c. 1595
Collection of Sven Gahlin
16.8 × 13cm

This early attribution is proposed by reason of its resemblance to the illustrations of birds in the *Bāburnāma* manuscripts. (See especially Suleiman (1970), nos. 55–86).

84

Mughal courtiers gaze in wonder at an ice lingam

c. 1600
Collection of M. Jean Soustiel, Paris
13.8 × 7.3cm

The lingam depicted here may be the stalagmite of ice at Amarnath in the Himalayas, which is an object of pilgrimage for Hindus.
Published:
1973 Soustiel p. 10 pl. 2

85

Musician playing the vina

By Manṣūr
c. 1600
Collection of E. Croft Murray, CBE, FSA
9 × 7.3cm

Inscribed bottom right-hand corner:
'*amal-i Manṣūr naqqāsh* (the work of Manṣūr the painter)

This is a rare portrait by Manṣūr who was famous for his paintings of flora and fauna. The subject is 'Alī Khān Karōrī, court musician to Akbar and Jahāngīr. He is portrayed in an illustration to the *Akbarnāma* (no. 46) and in a painting in the Museum of Fine Arts, Boston, which is inscribed 'Naubat Khān Kalāwant', a title conferred on him by Jahāngīr in 1607 (see Coomaraswamy (1930), no. LXIII, p. 39 and pl. XXVIII).

The painting at one time belonged to Panton Plymley, who was given it in 1790 by Jonathan

Scott, the orientalist and Persian secretary of Warren Hastings. This information is written on a slip of paper which has been pasted on the reverse of the painting and which unfortunately conceals what appears to be the seal of Shāh Jahān and possibly a description in Persian.

Published:
1950 Ashton no. 717 p. 159
1951 Gray p. 149 and fig. 6
1964 Welch pl. 18

80

86
Portrait of Mīrzā Yūsuf Khān
c. 1600
British Museum, 1948 10–9 074, bequeathed by P. C. Manuk and Miss G. M. Coles through the National Art Collections Fund
11.5 × 6cm

Inscribed on mount above painting:
Muḥammad Yūsuf Khān Akbar Shāhī...
(Muḥammad Yūsuf Khān (servant) of Akbar Shāh)

This is probably Mīrzā Yūsuf Khān Radavī, governor of Kashmir 1587–93. He died in 1601.

87
St John
By Abu'l-Ḥasan
Line-drawing enhanced with gold
1600
Ashmolean Museum, Reitlinger Collection
10.1 × 4.5cm

Signed by Abu'l-Ḥasan b. Rizā murīd-i-khānzād, in his thirteenth year, and dated 1009/1600. Because he is described as *khānzād* (born in the palace) we may assume that Āqā Rizā was already in Prince Salīm's service by 1588–9.

The figure of St John is copied from the engraving of Christ on the Cross in the Passion series by Albrecht Dürer.

Published:
1950 Ashton no. 665 pl. 128

88
The Virgin and Child
By Ghulām
c. 1600
British Museum, presented by the National Art Collections Fund, 1942 1–24 02
10.5 × 7cm

Inscribed:
raqm-i Ghulām-i Shāh Salīm
(drawing of Ghulam (servant) of Shāh Salīm)

This line-drawing, very lightly tinted and enhanced with gold, is probably after an original of the school of Bernart van Orley (1492–1542) through the medium of an engraving.

The artist must have been among those employed in the *atelier* of Prince Salīm, later Jahāngīr, who had his official residence at Allahabad from 1599–1604. The prince, in rebellion against his father, styled himself Shāh Salīm in 1600. Āqā Rizā signs himself in similar fashion on a portrait dated Ramazān, 1008 (see Godard (1936), p. 13f., fig. 2).

89

89

Christ's entry into Jerusalem

Illustration to the *Dastān-i Masīḥ* ('Life of Christ')

c. 1602

British Museum, 1965 7–24 05

14.8 × 7.3cm

Father Jerome Xavier, leader of the third Jesuit mission to the Mughal court, completed his *Dastān-i Masīḥ* in 1602, when it was presented to Akbar. It is known in seventeen extant manuscripts (see Maclagan (1932) p. 203f.; and Camps (1961) p. 168f.).

90

a. Moses and the plague of serpents

b. The Ascension

Illustrations to the *Dastān-i Masīḥ*

c. 1602

Collection of Edwin Binney

14.3 × 8cm and 18.3 × 8cm

These two miniatures come from the same manuscript as no. 89.

Published:

1973 Binney no. 28 a and b

91

Khusrau with a hawk

c. 1600

Collection of Sven Gahlin

Jahāngīr's eldest son Khusrau was born in 1586. The portrait is attributed on the reverse to Basāwan. For another portrait of Khusrau, see Stchoukine (1929) pl. XXIII (wrongly identified as Parvīz).

92

Raja Jagat Singh of Amber

c. 1600

Collection of Toby Falk

13.2 × 9cm

The identification is contained in two inscriptions, one in Devanagri, the other in Persian script, on the reverse. He was the eldest son of Raja Mān Singh of Amber. One of his daughters married Jahāngīr. He died in 1599.

For another portrait of Raja Jagat Singh, see Kühnel and Goetz (1926), pl. 37 (f. 18b).

93
Prince Dānyāl
c. 1605
British Museum, 1920 9–17 013(34)
12.4 × 7.6cm

The inscription *'amal-i Nādir al-Samarqandī* (the work of . . .) is probably a later addition, since the portrait must have been made in the lifetime of Prince Dānyāl or not long after his death in 1604. Born in 1572, he was the third son of Akbar.

94
a. The Last Judgement
By Nānhā and Manōhar
b. Scene in a garden
By Nar Singh
Miniatures (folios 5 verso and 6 recto) from a manuscript of the *Khamsa* of Mīr 'Alī Shīr Navā'ī copied at Herat by Sulṭān 'Alī of Mashhad in 897/1492.
c. 1605
The Royal Library, Windsor
23 × 15cm and 23.5 × 15.5cm

The manuscript found its way from Herat to Bukhara, where the miniatures were added, one (folio 36 verso) bearing the date 947/1540–1. According to an autograph note on the fly-leaf by Jahāngīr (folio 1 recto), the manuscript, 'one of my most treasured books', was entered in his library in the first year of his reign when 'the paintings were completed in my workshop'. In other words the original miniatures were entirely repainted by Jahāngīr's artists, Nar Singh, Nānhā, Govardhan and Manōhar. Another autograph note of Shāh Jahān (folio 1 recto), recording his possession of the manuscript, is dated 1037/1627–8, as also are his two seal impressions.

94a

The two miniatures bear no relation to the text of Navā'ī. In **a** the Last Judgement with Christ in Majesty; the Virgin on his right and St John the Baptist on his left. In the lower register, the Resurrection of the Dead. The painting must follow closely an engraving, probably after a late sixteenth-century original.

95
a. The poet 'Imād al-Dīn Faqīh
b. A youth joining a banquet
c. Dervishes dancing
d. A gathering of sages
e. Scene at a wine seller's
f. Jahāngīr playing polo
g. Jahāngīr while hunting meets an angel
h. Prince Khurram offering precious stones to his father Jahāngīr at Urta in 1607
Miniatures in a manuscript of the *Dīvān* of Ḥāfiẓ
c. 1610
British Library, Or. 7573
14 × 9.5cm (page), 10.2 × 6.4cm (miniature)

The subjects of **a** to **e** are more or less related to the text of Ḥāfiẓ. Of the three remaining miniatures, however, two commemorate Jahāngīr as polo player and hunter and one an occasion described in his memoirs. In **f** the figure in the upper right is Prince Khurram and in the lower right Prince Parvīz, behind Jahāngīr is Mīrzā Abu'l Ḥasan, Jahāngīr's brother-in-law and the brother of Nūr Maḥall. The subject of **g** is apparently inspired by the line in the ode (*ghazal*): 'Come, see! an angel has grasped his stirrup.' Stchoukine has identified the incident depicted in **h**. In 1607 Jahāngīr visited Kabul where his son Khurram had taken up his headquarters in the garden of Urta, and he describes in his memoirs the numerous gifts presented to him by his son. Parvīz stands immediately below and to the emperor's right. The occasion is also the subject of no. 112.

Published:
1929 Stchoukine pl. XXId
1931 Stchoukine pp. 160–7 figs. 1–4 6–9
1963 Barrett and Gray p. 100 (f.42r), p. 101 (f.66v)

96
Front cover of leather binding
Brown leather with blind tooled decoration; a central panel decorated with a frog and insects among flowering plants: in the border, cartouches containing palmettes and flowers
Period of Jahāngīr (1605–27)
Collection of M. Jean Soustiel, Paris
32 × 20.5cm

Published:
1974 Soustiel no. 10 (in colour)

97
A turkey cock
By Manṣūr
Page from the *Wantage Album*
Period of Jahāngīr (1605–27)
Victoria and Albert Museum, I.M. 135–1921
13.2 × 13cm (painting), 23.5 × 16.3cm (with margin)

Inscription on painting reads:
The work of the slave of the Threshold, Manṣūr Nādir al-'Aṣr, (servant) of Jahāngīr.

A turkey brought from Goa to Jahāngīr is described in his memoirs: Rogers (1909–14), I, p. 216.

98
A wild goat
Painting from the *Wantage Album*
By 'Ināyat
c. 1607
Victoria and Albert Museum, I.M. 138–1921
24.2 × 20cm (picture): 36.5 × 24.2cm (page)

Inscribed on border in Jahāngīr's hand:
the work of 'Ināyat

The creature is the markhor. Jahāngīr in his memoirs describes a remarkably large markhor with horns almost a metre and a half in length which he had painted by his artists (Rogers (1909–14), I, p. 112).

99
A chicken with her chicks
Painting on cotton
Period of Jahāngīr (1605–1628)
British Museum, bequeathed by Sir Edward Marsh, KCVO, CB, CMG, through the National Art Collections Fund, 1953 2–104 02
19 × 17.2cm

100
Hunting squirrels in a plane tree
c. 1610
India Office Library, *Johnson album* I no. 15
36.5 × 22.5cm

A hunter dressed in brown climbs the plane tree (*chenār*), the leaves of which range through green, russet and yellow; gazelles graze in the rocky background. The sky is gold.

An inscription on the reverse attributes the painting to Abu'l-Ḥasan Nādir al-'Aṣr, and Wilkinson (1948) has suggested that the artist's signature, originally in a small panel on the bottom left of the painting, was subsequently overpainted.

Published:
1924 Brown pl. XV
1948 Wilkinson pl. 6
1950 Ashton no. 737
1964 Welch pl. 35 (with detail in colour)

101

101

A young man holding a book
Early seventeenth century
British Museum, 1920 9–17 0281 (1)
15.3 × 8.9cm

This is a line-drawing, partially coloured (*nīm qalam*). The face is delicately modelled. The drawing has been attributed to Āqā Rizā and certainly bears the stamp of the contemporary Persian style which that artist introduced into Jahāngīr's *atelier*.

Published:
1925 Binyon pl. LIV (3)
1929 Blochet pl. CXCI

102

Bābur seated in a chair, reading a book
1605–10
British Museum, 1921 10–11 03
18.2 × 11.3cm

Inscribed on margin: *Shāh Bābur*

The style of costume and the turban are Persian. If the painting is not by Āqā Rizā himself, it is characteristic of the contemporary Persian style which he introduced.

Published:
1929 Stchoukine pl. XXXV(b)

103

A prince visiting a religious devotee
c. 1610
British Museum, 1920 9–17 04
18 × 12cm

The prince wears Persian costume; his six attendants are dressed in the style of the period of Akbar. The religious devotee holds a rosary (*tasbīḥ*); a dervish's crutch is lying by his side.

104

A mullā expounding in the courtyard of a mosque
c. 1610
British Museum, 1920 9–17 033
21.6 × 10.8cm

A *mullā* reads to three men, another is praying in the portico, while in the foreground a youth performs his ablutions. The rather bland palette is characteristic of the period of Jahāngīr.

Published:
1925 Binyon pl. LV (1)

105

The Virgin and child with a priest
c. 1610
British Museum, 1961 12–15 01, Brooke Sewell Fund
20.3 × 13cm

105

106
An album page composed of five miniatures mounted together:
a. Bābur
Seventeenth century
9.5 × 5.5cm
b. Dārāb Khān son of ʻAbd al-Raḥīm, Khān-i Khānān (d. 1625)
c. 1620
9.5 × 6.5cm
c. Sulṭān Parvīz (d. 1626)
1620–5
4 × 3.5cm
d. Afzal Khān Mullā Shukrullāh (d. 1639)
1610–25
4.8 × 3.8cm
e. Raja Mān Singh (d. 1614)
1600–25
12.5 × 6cm
British Museum, 1920 9–17 013 (38)

107
Prince holding a cup and flask
c. 1610
British Museum, 1949 12–10 010
11.5 × 6.5cm

108
A courtier
c. 1610
British Museum, bequeathed by P. C. Manuk and Miss G. M. Coles through the National Art Collections Fund, 1948 10–9 068
13.5 × 9.2cm

109
Jahāngīr in private audience
By Manōhar
c. 1605–6
British Museum, 1920 9–17 02
21 × 15.5cm

Inscribed on step of the dais:
Work (*ʻamal*) of Manōhar.

The scene is in the open air. Prince Khusrau offers wine to the emperor seated on a gold throne under a canopy supported by thin poles. Prince Parvīz stands behind Prince Khusrau. The two standing figures in the foreground – evidently high officers – have not been identified. The occasion is clearly an intimate one and distinct from the public durbar and the less formal audience in the *ghusal khāna*.

The presence of Khusrau suggests that this particular audience occurred soon after Jahāngīr's accession and before that prince's revolt in April 1606. Khusrau was rising twenty, his brother Parvīz two years his junior.

There is another and probably later version of this painting in the Institute of the Peoples of Asia, Leningrad: in this, the signature of Manōhar has been added; see Gyuzal'yan (1962), pl. 19.

Published:
1921 Binyon and Arnold pl. I (colour)

109

110
Calligraphic specimen of Prince Khurram
1611–12
Private collection
15 × 9.9cm

Four verses (*qiṭ'a*) preceded by the invocation: 'He [Allah] is the Self-sufficient' and signed in the fifth line: 'He who penned it [is] Sulṭān Khurram [in] the year 1020' (A.D. 1611–12).

Here am I tonight; Oh that thou were a companion such as I!
The company is spread out like a parterre:
The wine cup and happy converse and the minstrel – all are here:
Would that thou were here – and all the rest were nought.

Published:
1976 Skelton V 60

111

111
Parvīz received in audience by Jahāngīr
Painting from the *Minto Album*
c. 1614
Victoria and Albert Museum, I. M. 9–1925
21 × 15.5cm

The audience is probably that which took place on Prince Parvīz's appointment to the Deccan in 1609. He presents a cup to his father. The four courtiers in the row behind Parvīz are Mīrzā Rustam, Khān A'zam (d. 1624), Mīrzā Ghāzī (d. 1612) and Khān 'Ālam. Those in the front row are Āṣaf Khān, 'Abd-al-Raḥīm Khān-i Khānān, Khān Jahān Lodī, Raja Rām Dās Kachwāha and Murtazā Khān Shaykh Farīd Bukhārī (d. 1616).

The courtiers standing behind the emperor, reading from the top, are: Ani Rai Singh-dalan, Raja Bhao Singh of Amber (d. 1622), Raj Bīr Singh Deo, Maḥābat Khān (d. 1634), the Vazir 'Itimād al-Daula. The dark-skinned courtier has no identifying inscription.

The picture was painted probably just before Jahāngīr had his ears pierced for earrings in 1614, but after the granting of their titles to Āṣaf Khān and Raja Bhao Singh in the same year. The painting may be attributed to Manōhar (cf. no. 109).

Published:
1931 Stchoukine pl. LIV

112
Prince Khurram is weighed against gold and silver
Illustration to the *Tūzuk-ī Jahāngīrī* ('Memoirs of Jahāngīr')
c. 1615
British Museum, 1948 10–9 069, bequeathed by P. C. Manuk and Miss G. M. Coles through the National Art Collections Fund
26.6 × 20.5cm

The superscription reads: '. . . the whole day was passed in enjoyment and pleasure in the house of Bābā Khurram; and most of his presents were approved' (see Rogers (1909–14) I, p. 115).

The occasion was the celebration of Prince Khurram's sixteenth (lunar year) birthday by weighing him against gold and silver and other metals, which were then divided among the *faqīrs* and the poor. This took place in the Urta Garden during Jahāngīr's visit to Kabul in 1607. The occasion is also the subject of no. 95 (h).

The scales are set beneath a canopy. Two officials adjust the red bags containing money on the counter-balance, while a third is preparing further bags; holding the pan on which Khurram is seated is 'Abd al-Raḥīm Khān-i Khānān, and behind him, in descending order, are 'Itimād al-Daula, Āṣaf Khān, Maḥābat Khān and Khān Jahān Arā'ī. The last was Pīr Khān Lodi, given the title of Khān Jahān by Jahāngīr in 1607. He fell under the suspicion of Shāh Jahān and was killed in 1631.

The figure in the lower right foreground is recording the weight in a book. Among the gifts are jewelled belts, aigrettes, necklaces, vessels, daggers and sashes.

The painting cannot be earlier than 1614, when Jahāngīr had his ears pierced for earrings, but is certainly not later than 1615.

Published:
1963 Barrett and Gray pl. 103 (colour)

113
Audience of Jahāngīr
c. 1620
Painting from a manuscript of the *Tūzuk-i Jahāngīrī* ('Memoirs of Jahāngīr')
Private collection
29 × 20cm

An inscription behind the throne attributes the painting to Manōhar. Skelton (1976), p. 260, prefers to attribute it to Abu'l-Ḥasan. He suggests that the occasion illustrated here is the gift of the golden throne by 'Itimād al-Daula to Jahāngīr, and identifies the small boy whom Āṣaf Khān presents to Jahāngīr as one of the sons of Prince Khurram, either Dārā Shikōh or Shāh Shujā'.

Published:
1976 Skelton p. 259 pl. 127

114
Dervishes at night prepare food for Jahāngīr
By Abu'l-Ḥasan
Miniature from a manuscript of the *Tūzuk-i Jahāngīrī* ('Memoirs of Jahāngīr')
c. 1620
Collection of Edwin Binney
32.6 × 19.4cm

The miniature has been partially repainted. Binney (1973), no. 52, has suggested that the incident took place in the Shalimar Garden in Kashmir.

Published:
1973 Binney no. 52

115
Shāh 'Abbās I of Persia (1587–1629)
Attributed to Bishndās
1613–19
British Museum, 1920 9–17 013(2)
18.1 × 8.9cm

This particularly fine and well-observed portrait is attributed to the artist Bishndās, who accompanied the diplomatic mission led by Khān 'Ālam to Shāh 'Abbās in 1613. The mission remained in Persia until their return to India in 1619. Bishndās has recorded the mission in the well-known painting in the Museum of Fine Arts, Boston (see Coomaraswamy (1930), pp. 46–8, pl. XXXV). Bishndās, nephew of the painter Nānhā, was already active in the reign of Akbar; for a survey of his work see Das (1971), pp. 183–91.

Published:
1939 *Carmelites in Persia* I p. 285
1966 Blunt pl. 79

115

116
Album leaf with four portraits
a. Bust of Akbar at the audience window
Period of Jahāngīr (1605–27)
3.8 × 2.7cm
b. Bust portrait of Jahāngīr
c. 1610
3.8 × 2.7cm
c. Standing portrait of 'Abd al-Raḥīm Khān-i Khānān (1556-1627)
Period of Jahāngīr (1605–27)
9.8 × 5.6cm

Inscribed: *Khāni-i Khānān*

d. A page with a fly whisk (chauri)
Period of Jahāngīr (1605–27)
9.8 × 4.5cm

British Museum, 1920 9–17 013 (13)

117
Shāh Jahān
By Abu'l-Ḥasan Nādir al-Zamān
Painting from the *Minto Album*
c. 1616
Victoria and Albert Museum IM 14–1925
20.6 × 11.5cm (painting), 39 × 26.7cm (page)

Inscription beneath the painting in the hand of Shāh Jahān: 'A good portrait of me in my twenty-fifth year'

Published:
1971 Gascoigne p. 186

118
Krishna and the Paṇḍavas watering their horses
Miniature from a manuscript of the *Razmnāma*, copied in 1025/1616, now dispersed
c. 1616
British Museum, 1958 7–12 019, given by P. T. Brooke Sewell
36.9 × 21.8cm

In the lower margin there is an attribution to Kamāl, a painter whose work is represented in another copy of the *Razmnāma* made for 'Abd al-Raḥīm, Khān-i Khānān, in 1598–9, now in the Freer Gallery of Art, Washington; see Ettinghausen (1961), under pl. 4. 'Abd al-Raḥīm and other dignitaries are known to have possessed libraries with their own calligraphers and painters. The 1616 manuscript was no doubt the product of such a library, if not of the Khān-i Khānān's. For other miniatures from this manuscript, see Archer (1960), pl. 24; and Welch (1964), pl. 33.

Published:
1963 Barrett and Gray p. 106 (in colour)

119
A holy man in a landscape
Period of Jahāngīr (1605–27)
British Museum, 1960 2–13 01, Brooke Sewell Fund
14.5 × 8.7cm

It has been suggested that the subject may be that of Vāmana, the dwarf incarnation of Vishnu.

120

A prince and his companions listening to a singer

Attributed to Bishndās
c. 1613
Victoria and Albert Museum, I.S. 9–1965
20 × 14.5cm

If the attribution to Bishndās is accepted, then this painting would have been made just before his journey to Persia in 1613. The central figure might be Shāh Jahān, who in 1613 would have been twenty-three. Perhaps the harbour with European ships lying at anchor is that of Sūrat which at this time was included in Shāh Jahān's *jāgīr*.

Published:
1950 Ashton pl. H

117

116

121

A woodland scene

Period of Jahāngīr (1605–27)
British Museum, 1942 1–24 03
26 × 17.5cm

Based on a European landscape, this may have been inspired by the paintings of the Flemish artist Gillis van Coninxloo (1544–1607) or of the Dutch painter Jacob Savery (d. 1602), which would have become known to the Mughal painters through the engravings of Nicolas de Bruyn and others. This is confirmed by the cross-hatching on the tree trunks, which is otherwise unknown in Indian painting. The use of silver in rendering the water – now tarnished to a dull black – is common to Persian and Mughal painting.

119

122
A hunting cheetah being transported on a bullock cart
c. 1610–20
India Office Library, *Johnson Album* 67, no. 6
7.3 × 11.8cm

The attribution to Anupchatār was added later.

Published:
1950 Ashton no. 752 pl. 133

123
A lion
By Govardhan
c. 1615
Private collection
10 × 14.5cm

Attribution to Govardhan on the reverse. Line-drawings with pale washes such as this may have been preliminary studies for the finished paintings in the imperial albums.

124
Feeding an elephant
c. 1620
British Museum, 1939 5–13 013
20.7 × 28.9cm

Published:
1939 Gray pl. XXXI

125
The death of 'Ināyat Khān
Page from an album
c. 1618
Bodleian Library, Ouseley Add. 171 b 4 recto
12.5 × 15.3cm

'Ināyat Khān, an intimate of Jahāngīr, died in 1618 from over-indulgence in opium and wine. Jahāngīr tells in his memoirs how he directed his painters to record his death agonies. There is a sketch for this remarkable painting in the Museum of Fine Arts, Boston (cf. Coomaraswamy (1930), p. 42 and pl. LXX).

Published:
1921 Binyon and Arnold pl. XXIV
1924 Brown pl. L
1950 Ashton no. 733

126
The blue roller bird
c. 1620
Private collection
17.8 × 25cm

127
Portrait of Jahāngīr
c. 1620
Private collection
5.9 × 4.2cm

He is shown at a window against a dark ground. According to Skelton (1976) the globe and the key which he holds symbolize the opening of the secrets of the material and spiritual world to

120

God's regent, the emperor. For another portrait of this type see Gascoigne (1971), p. 114.

Published:
1976 Skelton V 69 pl. 126

128
Āṣaf Khān
By Bālchand
Painting from the *Wantage Album*
c. 1620
Victoria and Albert Museum, I.M. 120–1921
Inscribed in lower margin: the work of Bālchand

129
A European man and woman in a garden
Period of Janāngīr (1605–27)
British Museum, 1936 6–13 01
18 × 13.2cm

This is closely related to another painting of a Portuguese sailor and woman executed in a similar style (see Martin (1921), pl. 171; Welch (1959), p. 141 and fig. 14). If the sources of these studies of European manners were engravings, the Mughal artist has interpreted them in an entirely original way.

130
Muḥammad 'Alī Beg, Ambassador of Persia
Painting from the *Minto Album*
c. 1621
Victoria and Albert Museum, I.M. 25–1925
39 × 26.4cm (page), 22.8 × 14.6cm (painting)

Inscribed in Jahāngīr's own hand: A portrait of Muḥammad 'Alī Beg, ambassador, the work of Hāshim

He is not mentioned in the *Tūzuk-i Jahāngīrī* among the numerous embassies sent by the shah. He is represented wearing Persian dress.

128

131
Sulṭān Muḥammad Quṭb al-Mulk
Page from the *Minto Album*
c. 1625
Victoria and Albert Museum, IM 22–1925
36.8 × 26.4cm (page)

Inscribed in gold: 'The work of Hāshim', and inscribed in Jahāngīr's own hand: 'A good likeness of Sulṭān Muḥammad Quṭb al-Mulk'.

This is the only known contemporary portrait of Muḥammad Quṭb Shāh, King of Golconda (1579–1626) and is probably after a Deccani original.

132
Five sadhus seated by a fire
Attributed to Govardhan
c. 1625
Private collection
14.1 × 5.2cm

Published:
1973 Welch no. 63 (in colour)

133
Two travellers buying food in a village
By Mēv Das
Period of Jahāngīr (1605–27)
British Museum, 1920 9–17 0255
22 × 14cm

134
A keeper with a pair of deer
c. 1620
India Office Library, *Johnson Album* 67, no. 9
13.8 × 9.2cm

The flowers in the foreground, the iris on the hill and the foliage of the tree are later additions.

135
Portrait of Shāh Jāhān
1628
British Museum, 1969 3–17 01, presented by Mr and Mrs Anthony N. Sturt
19 × 14cm

Half-length in oval frame. The emperor stands facing right, holding in his left hand a seal on which are engraved his names and titles and the regnal year 1. Inscribed within oval to right: 'Written in the first [year] of the blessed reign; brought to the attention of His Majesty while hunting.' The framing inscription extracted from a manuscript of the *Tūzuk* has been added.

Shāh Jāhān was thirty-six on his accession in 1628.

Published:
1950 Ashton no. 753, pl. 136

129

130

131

133

134

136
Shāh Jahān
Page from *Minto Album*
c. 1631
Victoria and Albert Museum, I.M. 17–1925
22.3 × 13.3cm (painting),
38.8 × 26.8cm (album page)

Inscribed in the hand of Shāh Jahān: A good portrait of me in my fortieth year, the work of Bichitr

Published:
1964 Welch pl. 43

137
Prince Salīm
By Bichitr
Page from the *Minto Album*
c. 1630
Victoria and Albert Museum, I.M. 28–1925
25 × 18.1cm (painting),
38.8 × 26.4cm (album page)

Inscribed in lower margin: Drawing (*raqm*) by Bichitr

This posthumous portrait of Jahāngīr was presumably after an earlier original.

Published:
1968 Hambly p. 72

138
Tīmūr enthroned with the first four Mughal emperors
By Hāshim
Period of Shāh Jahān (1628–58)
India Office Library, *Johnson Album* nos. 64–38
17.4 × 11.6cm

Tīmūr is seated on a throne beneath a parasol (*chatra*). Bābur and Akbar are enthroned on his right, Humāyūn and Jahāngīr on his left. The shaykh who offers a book to Tīmūr can be identified as the poet Sa'dī, since the same figure appears in a miniature, 'Sa'dī and other Sufis led to an imperial audience', now in the Walters Art Gallery, Baltimore (see Ettinghausen (1961), fig. 2). It has been suggested that Jahāngīr's notion of kingship and his preoccupation with dervishes found sanction in Sa'dī's work (see Ettinghausen (1961), p. 114).

Published:
1950 Ashton no. 759

138

139

140

139
Shāh Jahān and Dārā Shikōh on horseback
By Govardhan
Page from the *Minto Album*
c. 1632
Victoria and Albert Museum, I.M. 18–1925
22.3 × 14cm (painting), 38.8 × 26.4cm (page)

Inscribed in lower margin: the work of Govardhan

Before the *Minto Album* was dismantled, facing this page was a similar composition of Tīmūr and attendant, both on horseback, the latter holding a parasol. The painting is now in the Chester Beatty Library (Arnold (1936) III, pl. 55). The original confrontation of the two paintings depicting the 'First and Second Lords of the Happy Conjunction', i.e., Tīmūr and Shāh Jahān, was deliberate.

Published:
1968 Hambly no. 63

140
Calligraphic specimen by Dārā Shikōh
1630
Victoria and Albert Museum, I.S. 37–1972
21.5 × 19.8cm (text), 40 × 25.5cm (page)

Inscribed in small writing in four panels: 'Written in Burhanpur in the year 1040, the third regnal year' (equivalent to 1630). Although the name of the scribe is not given, we may assume it to be that of Dārā Shikōh, since similar writing signed by him occurs on other pages of the album from which this one was extracted.

The text consists of verses giving a chronology of the Prophet and the Orthodox Caliphs.

141
Equestrian portrait of Dārā Shikōh
c. 1633
Private collection
31 × 21cm

Skelton (1976) has identified the occasion of this portrait as Dārā Shikōh's marriage to the daughter of his uncle, Sulṭān Parvīz, in 1633.

142
Aurangzīb and Murād Bakhsh
c. 1635
British Museum, 1920 9–17 0287
20.3 × 13.5cm

This consists of two separate miniatures skilfully mounted as one. Murād Baksh is on the left, Aurangzīb, on a smaller scale, is on the right. These fine portraits were probably made from the life. Murād Bakhsh was born in 1624, Aurangzīb in 1618.

The dark ground was probably added later.

143
Calligraphic specimen with illuminated border
Illuminated border by Daulat
Page from the *Minto Album*
c. 1630
Victoria and Albert Museum, I.M. 24–1925 (verso)
38.8 × 26.4cm

Inscribed on lower border: 'The work of the illuminator the indigent [*faqīr*] Daulat'. Besides painting borders, Daulat contributed miniatures to a manuscript of the *Bāburnāma* now in the National Museum, New Delhi, dated 1597 and to the manuscript of the *Akbarnāma* in the Chester Beatty Library.

144
The rebuke of the old man
Miniatures (folio 129 recto) in a manuscript of Sa'dī's *Bustān*, copied by Ḥakīm Rukn al-Dīn Maṣ'ūd at Agra in 1039/1629.

British Library, Add. 27262
8 × 15.4cm

The scribe Rukn al-Dīn was of Persian origin and was a poet who was highly esteemed by Shāh Jahān. In the following year he made a copy of Sa'dī's *Gulistān*, a companion to our volume. This manuscript, now in the Chester Beatty Library, Dublin, contains an autograph entry by Shāh Jahān dated 1638, stating that he has sent it as a gift to the King of England (Charles I) (see Wilkinson (1957), pp. 423–5).

The volume in the British Library contains ten miniatures. Each page is enhanced with gold marginal decorations. Illustrated manuscripts of literary works of this quality are rare after the period of Jahāngīr.

Published:
1957 Pinder-Wilson pp. 415–18 and fig. 9

142

145
A Maulvi meditating
c. 1630
British Museum, 1949 2–12 05
17.2 × 10.6cm

Published:
1950 Ashton no. 769
1963 Barrett and Gray p. 111 (in colour)

146
A prince stalking deer by night
c. 1630
Bodleian Library, Ouseley Add. 171b 6 recto
12.5 × 15.3cm

This night scene is set in a rocky landscape with trees and a stream. A prince and two companions crouch on a rocky ledge by a pool. He directs a shaft from his bow at the deer, which are attracted by the torch held by the companion on his left.

Published:
1921 Binyon and Arnold pl. XXXIV
1924 Brown pl. XLIV

147
Lovers on a terrace
By Bālchand
c. 1635
Private collection
22.5 × 13.1cm

Inscribed below carpet: the work of Bālchand

Bālchand's earliest work is in the *Akbarnāma* of 1600–08 in the Chester Beatty Library (see Arnold (1936), II, pl. 24). In the 'Lovers on a Terrace' there are similarities in the treatment of turbans and carpet, as well as in the palette to Bālchand's last recorded miniature, a *durbar* scene (folio 43 verso) in the manuscript of the *Shāhjahānnāma* (see no. 167). Bālchand has included a portrait of himself in this *durbar* scene, a man of about sixty-five with a full white beard and dark eyebrows.

Published:
1973 Welch no. 65
1975 Beach pl. 1

148
Sa'dī talks with a friend in a garden
By Govardhan
Miniature (folio 5 recto) in a manuscript of Sa'dī's *Gulistān* copied by Sulṭān 'Alī Mashhadī on 11 Rabī' II, 873/29 October 1468 at Herat
c. 1535
Collection of the Marquess of Bute
12 × 7cm

The attribution to Govardhan in the lower margin has been partially effaced.

At some time the manuscript was damaged by water and remarginated in Persia, where the border illuminations were added. The manuscript was once again damaged by water and the six original miniatures repainted by the group of artists who painted the miniatures in the *Shāhjāhānnāma*, now in the Royal Library (167). On the fly-leaf there are notes of possession by Jahāngīr, Shāh Jahān, Dārā Shikōh and Shāh Jahān's eldest daughter, Jahānārā.

The subject of the miniature is the opening episode of the *Gulistān*. Sa'dī meets his friend carrying flowers and reminds him that they will perish, while he will create a literary rose garden (*gulistān*) which will be imperishable.

149
A gathering of ascetics
By 'Ināyat
Dated A.D. 1630–1
British Museum, 1941 7–12 05
22 × 15cm

Signed in bottom left: 'the humblest servant of the Lord of the Second Conjunction, 'Ināyat, year 1040 A.H.' (A.D. 1630–1).

Published:
1948 Wilkinson pl. 10

149

150
Ṣādiq Khān
By Govardhan
c. 1630
British Museum, 1920 9–17 013(3)
16 × 10.2cm

Inscribed: '*amal-i Govardhan* (the work of Govardhan).

Ṣādiq Khān, *mīr bakhshī* (paymaster-general) under Jahāngīr and Shāh Jahān, died in 1633.

Published:
1921 Binyon and Arnold pl. XXVII

152

151
Āṣaf Khān
c. 1630
British Museum, 1965 7–24 06, Brooke Sewell Fund
18.3 × 9.5cm

Mīrzā Abu'l-Ḥasan received successively the titles I'timād Khān, Āṣaf Khān, Yamīn al-Daula and Khān-i Khānān. He was the brother of Nūr Jahān and father of Mumtaz Maḥall, the wife of Shāh Jahān. He died in 1641.

152
Āṣaf Khān as commander-in-chief
By Bichitr
Page from the *Minto Album*
c. 1635
Victoria and Albert Museum, I.M. 26–1925
24.6 × 16.3cm (painting),
38.8 × 26.4cm (album page)

Inscribed in lower margin: 'Āṣaf Khan, Khān-i Khānān, commander-in-chief (*sipah-sālār*), the work of Bichitr.' An inscription on the scroll held by the angel in the sky reads: 'Allah is greatest, help is from Allah, victory is near, the [regnal] year 3 (1630–1).' At this time Āṣaf Khān was in command of the troops invading Bijapur and Gulbarga.

Published:
1960 Archer pl. 27 (in colour)
1968 Hambly p. 91 (in colour)

153
A nobleman
c. 1635
Collection of Sven Gahlin
20.8 × 11cm

The figure may be that of Mu'taqid Khān, governor of Malwa, whose portrait occurs in the *Shāhjahānnāma* manuscript (167).

154
Mīrzā Nūr al-Ḥasan
By Hūnhār
British Museum, 1920 9–17 013(23)
22.9 × 12.1cm

Inscribed on miniature: *'amal-i Hūnhār* (the work of Hūnhār).

The subject is described on the reverse of the leaf as Mīrzā Nūr al-Ḥasan, son of Mīrzā Muḥsin, son of Āṣaf Khān Ja'far, and on the lower mount, *Mīrzā Abu'l Ḥasan ibn-i' amm* [*cousin of*] *Āṣaf Khan*. Neither name seems to be recorded. The identification of the portrait by Binyon and Arnold (1921), p. 84 as Abu'l Ḥasan Āṣaf Khān as a young man is unconvincing, since the features portrayed here bear little or no relation to those of the mature Āṣaf Khān as portrayed in nos. 151 and 152.

Published:
1912 Martin pl. 192
1921 Binyon and Arnold pl. XXIX

154

155
Allāhvardī Khān
By Hūnhār
Period of Shāh Jahān (1628–58)
British Museum, 1920 9–17 013(8)
18.4 × 11.4cm

Inscribed: *'amal-i Hūnhār* (the work of Hūnhār)

Allāhvardī Khān, a noble of the court of Jahāngīr, was raised to the rank of five thousand by Shāh Jahān. In the war of the succession he was chief adviser of Shāh Shujā'. Aurangzīb, however, suborned him and he was put to death by Shujā' in 1659.

Published:
1912 Martin pl. 193

156
Mīrzā Nauzar
By Mīr Hāshim
Period of Shāh Jahān (1627–58)
British Museum, 1920 9–17 013 (40)
22.9 × 12.1cm

Inscribed: *'amal-i Mīr Hāshim* (the work of Mīr Hāshim)

Mīrzā Nauzar was the son of Mīrzā Haydar and a favourite of Shāh Jahān. He died in 1664.

Published:
1912 Martin pl. 185

157
Ḥakīm Ṣadrā
By Hāshim
Period of Shāh Jahān (1628–58)
British Museum, 1920 9–17 013 (20)
21.3 × 10.8cm

Inscribed: *'amal-i Hāshim* (the work of Hāshim)

Head and shoulders only. Line-drawing lightly tinted.

Ḥakīm Ṣadrā went to India in 1601, where he served as doctor both to Akbar and Jahāngīr. In 1609 he was granted the title *Masīḥ al-Zamān*, 'Messiah of the Age', by Jahāngīr. He died in 1650.

Published:
1912 Martin pl. 185
1924 Brown pl. LXV fig. 1

158
Dārā Shikōh
By Chitarman
c. 1640
Page from the *Minto Album*
Victoria and Albert Museum, I.M. 19–1925
24.7 × 16cm (painting)
38.8 × 26.4cm (whole leaf)

Inscribed by Shāh Jahān: A good likeness of Bābā Dārā Shikōh painted by Chitarman

He wears a white *angarkha* and mauve trousers and holds a red tray, possibly of red lacquer, on which are pieces of jewellery, including a black and white cameo. He is decked with ropes of pearls; jade archer's rings and a knife are attached to his belt.

159
Shāh Shujā'
By Lāl Chand
Painting from the *Minto Album*
c. 1640
Victoria and Albert Museum, I.M. 15–1925
15.4 × 18.8cm (painting),
38.8 × 26.4cm (album leaf)

Shāh Jahān's second son, Shāh Shujā', was born in 1616.

160
Sages in a landscape
Paintings from an album
c. 1645
Edwin Binney
23.1 × 17.1cm (painting)
39.1 × 25.9cm (album leaf)

Published:
1973 Binney no. 60

161
Singer and musicians
By Bichitr
Painting from the *Minto Album*
c. 1645
Victoria and Albert Museum, I.M. 27–1925
18.8 × 12cm (painting)
38.8 × 26.8cm (page)

Inscribed in Shāh Jahān's hand in lower margin: the work of Bichitr

162
Portrait of a horse, 'Amber Head'
c. 1650
British Museum, 1920 9–17 03
31.7 × 23.5cm

Inscribed between legs: *shabih-i anbar sar* (portrait of Amber Head)

163
The adoring lover
c. 1650
British Museum, 1920 9–17 0262
20 × 26.5cm

A young man kneels before a couch on which is seated a girl. She is attended by a maid.

The upper carpet, consisting of a gold design on a white ground, is an Aubusson type which was current after 1640.

Published:
1929 Stchoukine pl. LVI

162

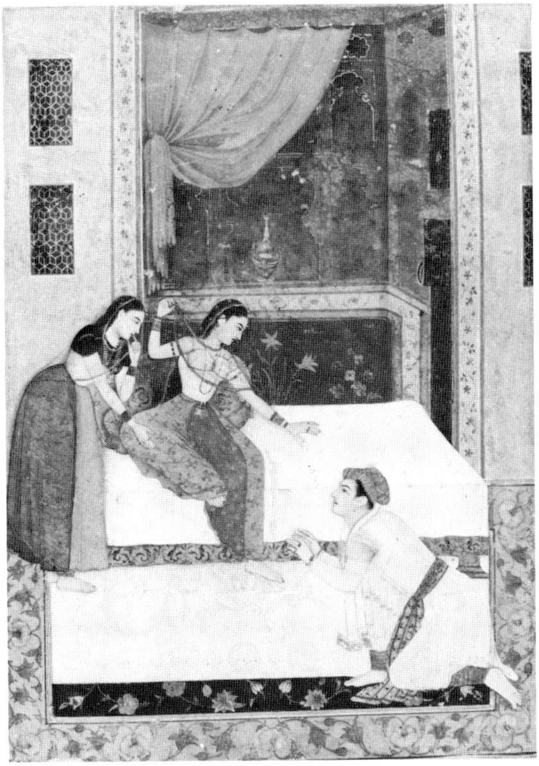

163

165

164
Mystics seated by a fire
By Payāg
c. 1655
Private collection
19.7 × 13.2cm

The earliest work of Payāg, brother of Bālchand, is in the *Bāburnāma* manuscript of 1597 in the National Museum, New Delhi. His style is distinctive and lacks the hardness of many of his contemporaries. In 1655 he must have been at least seventy years old.

Published:
1976 Skelton V72

165
Shāh Jahān in old age
c. 1650
British Museum, 1920 9–17 013(16)
22 × 15cm

The emperor is represented in court costume bearing a sword on his right shoulder. He appears to be about sixty years old.

Published:
1929 Stchoukine pl. XXXVII (a)

166
Khwāja Abu'l-Ḥasan Turbatī
1658
British Museum, 1942 10–10 02
16 × 8cm

According to the inscription on the reverse of the leaf, the portrait was executed by the painter '. . . . Dās' after an original by Hāshim, and presented by a certain 'Ināyat Khān to a child of Sakīna Bānū Khānum in 1068/1657–8. There is a standing portrait by Hāshim of Khwāja Abu'l-Ḥasan in the Louvre (see Stchoukine (1929), pl. XXXI) and he is included in a *durbar* group of Shāh Jahān in a manuscript of 1663 (see Pinder-Wilson (1957), fig. 13). This last, like the seated portrait under discussion, is posthumous, since Khwāja Abu'l Ḥasan died in 1632. He served in the *dīvān* of the Deccan under Akbar, and successively as *mīr bahkshi, dīvān-i-kull* and governor of Kabul under Jahāngīr and Shāh Jahān.

167
Shāh Jahān's reception of his sons, Dārā Shikōh, Muḥammad Shujā' and Aurangzīb with Āṣaf Khān at Agra in 1628
By Bichitr
Double miniature (pp. 101, 102) from a manuscript of the *Shāhjahānnāma* by 'Abd al-Ḥamīd of Lahore, copied by Muḥammad Amīn of Mashhad in 1067/1657–8.
The Royal Library, Windsor
Each miniature 30.5 × 21.5cm

The occasion is commemorated in the inscription below the cornice above the emperor's throne. Shāh Jahān's formal accession took place on 28 January 1628. On 26 February Āṣaf Khān arrived from Lahore with the three princes, and on the following day the party was formally received by the emperor.

The emperor, seated on the balcony (*jharoka-i darshan*), embraces his third son Aurangzīb, behind whom stand Dārā Sikōh and Shāh Shujā', the eldest and second sons. The fourth son, Murād Bakhsh, stands to the right of the emperor.

Published:
1971 Gascoigne p. 145 (reproduces p. 101 in colour)

Paintings from the Muslim Courts of the Deccan

The history of the three Muslim states of the Deccan – Ahmadnagar, Bijapur and Golconda – makes a striking contrast with that of the Mughals. None of the Deccan kingdoms shared the imperial ambitions of Akbar and his successors. Indifferent, it seems, to the danger threatening from the north, they preferred to bicker with each other until they were finally absorbed by the Mughal Empire. Ineffectual in policy and war, the Deccan rulers were in the main highly cultivated men – several were poets of merit – and generous patrons, filling their days with careless enjoyment (for which they seem to have had a natural talent) of the civilized pleasures to hand.

This contrast with the purpose and values of the Mughal is reflected in the paintings. There is in Deccan painting no element of propaganda – they did not see themselves as newcomers to the Indian scene – and little of official display. There were no highly organized *ateliers*: the output seems to have been comparatively small and the group exhibited represents perhaps a third of the finest paintings to have survived. There are no illustrated histories to extol the ruler and his house, and the Deccan artist did not attempt the vigorous narrative style of the Mughal. Using much the same sources as the Mughal – Persian, native Indian and European – the Deccan artists swiftly achieved fully integrated styles in which, as in Persia, colour and design were employed for emotive purposes, to create a mood. This is especially clear in the portraits. One is made aware not of the monarch or great courtier but of the expression of a personality caught in a moment of complete self-absorption. This mysterious sympathy is communicated by the subtle placing and scale of the figures and by the distinctive palette. The colour range, in both clear and sombre tones, is an original contribution by the Deccan artist, and is nowhere employed to more melting effect than on the exquisite finery worn by the men, where all colours are muted by the white transparent cotton coats.

Compared with the more ambitious Mughal, the range of the Deccan artist is deliberately restricted, but his mode of expression, intimate and effortless, gave his actual achievement a unique position in the history of Indian painting.

168
The Enraged Elephant
Deccan, perhaps Ahmadnagar
c. 1605
Collection of Edwin Binney
28.5 × 20.9cm

Published:
1973 Binney no. 119 (colour)

169
Portrait of a noble
Deccan, perhaps Ahmadnagar
c. 1610
British Museum, 1959 7–11 01, Brooke Sewell Fund
22.8 × 11cm

170
Lady hawking on horseback
Deccan, perhaps Ahmadnagar
c. 1620
India Office Library, *Johnson Album* 67, no. 3
29.7 × 22.1cm

The lady is accompanied by a groom and a black and white hound. The scene is set in a flowery meadow enclosed in a winding brook and dominated by a *chenār* tree. Against the gold sky is a white palace or hunting lodge.

Published:
1960 Archer pl. 17

171
Lovers on a terrace
Miniature (folio 199 recto) in a manuscript of the *Pem-nem* ('The Lore of Love')
Bijapur
1590–1
British Library, Add. 16880

This is a unique copy of a poem written in Deccani Urdu by Ḥasan Manjhu Khaljī, who assumed the pen name of Hans. The poem includes a eulogy of Ibrāhīm 'Ādil Shāh II, his learning, penmanship and knowledge of music.

Published:
1969 Barrett p. 151

172

172
Horse and Groom
Painting from an album
Bijapur
c. 1605
Victoria and Albert Museum, I.S. 88–1965
11.4 × 10.3cm (painting),
40.5 × 27cm (album page)

The illumination is contemporary.

173
Ibrāhīm 'Ādil Shāh (1580–1627)
Bijapur
c. 1610
Collection of Edwin Binney
19 × 9.8cm

Published:
1973 Binney no. 112

174
Portrait of a noble
Bijapur
c. 1615
British Museum, 1937 4–10 03
17 × 10cm

Lower and possibly upper edge have been trimmed.

Published:
1938 Gray p. 76 and pl. C;
1963 Barrett and Gray p. 126

175

175
Portrait of a courtier
Bijapur
c. 1615
India Office Library *Johnson Album* 25, no. 14 (J. 25–14)
14.8 × 7.5cm

The elderly bearded courtier holds a book in his right hand and, in his left, a rosary and a blue, gold-decorated staff. He wears a folded shawl over his shoulders. At his feet are two partridges and a flowering iris.

Published:
1950 Ashton no. 813 pl. 145

176
Portrait of a musician
Bijapur
c. 1615
British Museum, 1937 4–10 02
17 × 10.2cm

This is perhaps the finest picture to have survived from the school of Bijapur. Indeed this dignified figure has often been identified with Ibrāhīm ʿĀdil Shāh II of Bijapur (1580–1627).

He wears the splendid finery of the Deccan and holds in his left hand a pair of stained ivory castanets.

Published:
1938 Gray p. 75f pl. B

177
Study of a Carnation
Deccan, probably Bijapur
c. 1625
Collection of Sven Gahlin
19.8 × 12cm

178
Portrait of Muḥammad 'Ādil Shāh (1627–1656)
Bijapur
c. 1640
British Museum, 1937 4–10 04
14.8 × 11.3cm

The successor to Ibrāhīm II, Muḥammad came to the throne at the age of fifteen. In this portrait he appears to be about twenty-eight. He holds a *champak* blossom in one hand and a mango in the other.

Published:
1958 Barrett p. 22 and pl. 9

179
Muḥammad 'Ādil Shāh (1627–1656)
Bijapur
c. 1645
Private collection
26.7 × 30.5cm

The king, who appears a little older than in the portrait (no. 178), is acting as mahout to the splendidly caparisoned elephant. He is accompanied by an Abyssinian fan-bearer. On the left a vertical inscription attributes the picture to the artists Haydar 'Alī and Ibrāhīm Khān.

179

180
Ibrāhīm 'Ādil Shāh (1580–1627) feeding a bird
Bijapur
Late seventeenth century
Private collection
24.7 × 18cm

Inscribed on label pasted to the lower border '*Ibrāhīm 'Ādil Shāh*'. The large fan carries an inscription: *Ustād-i ṣāḥib-i salāmat* (Lord of Salvation)

This is a late seventeenth century copy, perhaps Mughal, of a Bijapur painting of about 1610.

Published:
1960 Archer pl. 16

181
Enthroned king watching dancers
Golconda
c. 1586–90
British Museum, 1974 6–17 06(1)
17 × 8.4cm

This and nos. 2–5 were inserted in a manuscript of the *Dīvān* of Ḥāfiẓ dated A.D. 1643 in the British Library (Add. 16762). The king in all five paintings is probably Muḥammad Qulī Quṭb Shāh (1580–1611), who ascended the throne at the age of fourteen. The scene is set in a tented camp. The king, enthroned under a canopy, is flanked by his cup-bearer and sword-bearer. He and his court watch the performers, who dance to the accompaniment of a drummer and to the clapping of some of the courtiers.

Published:
1960 Barrett p. 10 fig. 1

182
The king watching dancers
Golconda
c. 1586–90
British Museum, 1974 6–17 06(2)
17 × 8.5cm

The king and his court are watching the dancers. They are seated before the gold throne, which stands beneath a canopy and is surrounded by gold plate and two gold elephants. The two elaborately balustered gold tables have circular silver tops bordered by red velvet. Two courtiers hold the royal children.

Published:
1960 Barrett p. 11 fig. 2

183
Scene in a pavilion of the royal harem
Golconda
c. 1586–90
British Museum, 1974 6–17 06(3)
17 × 8.5cm

Above, the king is carousing with his women, one of whom massages his leg. Below, a lady is watching a dance performance. She too is carousing and may be Muḥammad Qulī's favourite, the beautiful Hindu dancing-girl Bhāgmatī.

Published:
1960 Barrett p. 11 fig. 3

184
A royal picnic
Golconda
1586–90
British Museum, 1974 6–17 06(4)
17 × 8.7cm

The king is reclining on his throne with his leg being massaged and surrounded by his women. Before him is an ornamental pool. Below the dancers, servants are preparing the feast.

Published:
1960 Barrett p. 11 fig. 4

185
The king seated in state
Golconda
1586–90
British Museum, 1974 6–17 06(5)
21.2 × 10.7cm

In the top field the king is seated holding a long sword and flanked by his cup-bearer and fan (*chaurī*)-bearer. In the middle field are four seated men one of whom – a poet perhaps – seems about to recite. In the lower field two women are dancing to the accompaniment of an Abyssinian orchestra.

Published:
1960 Barrett p. 11 fig. 5

186
Reception of ambassadors by the King of Golconda
Golconda
1611 or 1626
British Museum, 1937 4–10 01
25 × 15.5cm

The attention of the youthful king is directed to the two standing figures, one of whom bears in his upraised hand a letter while the other holds a finger to his mouth – a conventional gesture of wonder and admiration. Below them a kneeling dignitary holds a thin white object which is probably a pen-case. To the left of the king are his two fan-bearers – one an Abyssinian – and his cup-bearer. In the lower foreground are four horses and their grooms.

There is in this fine painting a sense of actuality which suggests that the painter is commemorating a particular occasion. The two standing figures are dressed in the costume of the Deccan. If they are, as we believe, ambassadors, they are the representatives of the kingdoms of Ahmadnagar and Bijapur. The presence of the horses – a common gift between Muslim kings – supports this hypothesis.

The young king may be Muḥammad Quṭb Shāh, who came to the throne in 1611 at the age of eighteen, or his son 'Abdullāh, who succeeded in 1626 at the age of twelve. His angular features seem to resemble those of the mature Muḥammad in a fine contemporary Mughal portrait in the Victoria and Albert Museum, the only known certain likeness of Muḥammad (no. 131). They do not resemble in any way those of 'Abdullāh as known to us in later portraits of him as a young man and in middle age. The distinctive white costume with broad gold borders is also worn by Muḥammad in the Victoria and Albert Museum portrait and seems to have been affected only by him and his predecessor Muḥammad Qulī. However the kneeling figure with the white beard resembles later portraits in old age of Shaykh Muḥammad ibn Khātūn, who was the private secretary of Muḥammad and prime minister under 'Abdullāh. Though his dates are uncertain, he seems to have died in the 1640s. If this is sufficient reason for identifying the young king as 'Abdullāh, then we have to propose that the picture represents the two ambassadors (Mīr Ja'far and Shāh Abu'l Ḥasan) and their valuable presents sent in 1626 to offer condolence and congratulations from Ahmadnagar and Bijapur.

Published:
1958 Barrett p. 20 pl. VIII
1973 Skelton pp. 184–7

187
Portrait of a Golconda king
Golconda
c. 1620
Private collection

The king, wearing the costume affected by Muḥammad Qulī (1580–1611) and his nephew and successor Muḥammad (1611–26), rests his right hand on his long straight-bladed sword and holds a nosegay of roses in his left. We believe that the subject is Muḥammad.

188
A Yogini or Female Devotee
Deccan, perhaps Golconda
c. 1650
Private collection
18.2 × 9.4cm

Inscribed: *'amal-i pardesī* (work of a foreigner).

Published:
1976 Skelton no. V.100 and pl. 41 (in colour)

187

189
Landscape with tall flowering plants
Deccan, perhaps Golconda
c. 1650
Private collection
20.8 × 12cm

Published:
1976 Skelton no. V.99 and pl. 4 (in colour)

190
Eight pages with illuminated borders
Folios (5 verso, 6 verso, 10 verso, 11 recto, 16 recto, 19 verso, 28 verso, 29 recto) from a manuscript of a poem in praise of 'Abdullāh Quṭb Shāh (1626–74) of Golconda copied by 'Alī ibn Naqī al-Ḥusayni Dāmghāni.
Golconda
c. 1650
British Library, Or. 13533
28 × 18cm

Bibliography

Archer, W. G.
1960. *Indian Miniatures,* London.
Arnold, Sir Thomas
1928. *Painting in Islam,* Oxford.
1936. *The Library of A. Chester Beatty. A Catalogue of the Indian Miniatures,* London.
Ashton, Sir Leigh (ed.)
1950. *The Art of India and Pakistan, a commemorative catalogue of the exhibition held at the Royal Academy of Arts, London, 1947–48,* London.

Barrett, Douglas
1958. *Painting of the Deccan XVI–XVII century,* London.
1960. 'Some unpublished Deccan Miniatures', *Lalit Kalā,* VII, pp. 9–13.
1969. 'Painting at Bijapur', *Paintings from Islamic Lands,* Oxford, pp. 142–59.
Barrett, Douglas and **Gray, Basil**
1963. *Painting of India,* Lausanne.
Beach, M.
1975. 'The Context of Rajput Painting', *Ars Orientalis,* X, pp. 11–19.
Beach, M. *et al.*
1966. *The Arts of India and Nepal: the Nasli and Heeramaneck Collections,* Boston.
Beeston, A. F. L.
1953–5. 'The Atkinson Lailâ Majnûn', *Bodleian Library Record,* 4, pp. 63–6.
Beveridge, A. S.
1922. *The Babur-nama in English,* London.
Beveridge, H.
1902. *The Akbarnama of Abu'l-Fazl,* Calcutta.
Binney III, Edwin
1973. *Indian Miniature Painting from the Collection of Edwin Binney, 3rd: 1. The Mughal and Deccani School with some related Sultanate material,* an exhibition at the Portland Art Museum, 1 December 1973 – 20 January 1974.
Binyon, Laurence and **Arnold, T. W.**
1921. *The Court Painters of the Grand Moguls,* London.
Binyon, Laurence
1925. 'Asiatic Art in the British Museum (Sculpture and Painting),' *Ars Asiatica,* VI, Paris.
1930. *Emperors and Princes of the House of Timur,* British Museum.
Blochet, E.
1929. *Musulman Painting XIIth–XVIIth century,* London.
Blunt, Wilfrid
1966. *Isfahan: Pearl of Persia,* London.
Brown, Percy
1924. *Indian Painting under the Mughals, AD 1550 to AD 1750,* Oxford.

Camps, Arnulf
1961. 'Persian works of Jerome Xavier, a Jesuit at the Mogul Court',

Islamic Culture, XXXV, pp. 166–76.
Carmelites in Persia
1939. *A chronicle of the Carmelites in Persia and the Papal Mission of the XVIIth and XVIIIth Centuries,* London.
Clarke, C. Stanley
1921. *Indian Drawings: twelve Mogul Paintings of the School of Humayun (16th century); illustrating the Romance of Amīr Hamzah,* London.
1922. *Indian Drawings, Thirty Mogul Paintings of the School of Jahangir (17th century) and four panels of calligraphy in the Wantage Bequest, Victoria and Albert Museum Portfolios,* London.
Coomaraswamy, A. K.
1930. *Catalogue of the Indian Collections in the Museum of Fine Arts, Boston, Pt. VI Mughal Painting,* Cambridge, Mass.

Das, Asok Kumar
1971. 'Bishndās', *Chhavi, Golden Jubilee Volume, Bharat Kala Bhavan 1920–1970,* Banaras, pp. 183–91.
1975. 'Ustad Mansur', *Lalit Kalā,* XVII, pp. 32ff.

Ettinghausen, Richard
1961. 'The Emperor's choice', *Essays in Honor of Erwin Panofsky,* ed. M. Meiss, New York.

Gascoigne, B.
1971. *The Great Moghuls,* London.
Glück, Heinrich
1925. *Die Indischen Miniaturen des Haemza–Romanes in Osterreichischen Museum für Kunst und Industrie in Wien und in Anderen Sammlungen.* Zurich, Vienna and Leipzig.
Glynn, Catherine
1974. 'An Early Mughal Landscape Painting and Related Works', *Los Angeles County Museum of Art Bulletin,* XX, pp. 65–72.
Godard, Y. A.
1925. 'Les Marges du Murakka Gulshan', *Athār-e Irān,* I, pp. 11–33.
Gray, B.
1934. 'An early Mughal illuminated page', *British Museum Quarterly,* VIII: 4, pp. 149–51.
1938. 'Deccani paintings: The School of Bijapur', Burlington Magazine, LXXXIII.
1938–9. 'A Mughal Drawing', *British Museum Quarterly,* XIII, pp. 72f, pl. XXXI.
1951. 'Islamic Art at the Indian Exhibition. Royal Academy, London, November 1947 to February 1948', *Ars Islamica,* XV–XVI, pp. 145–9.
Gyuzal'yan, L. T. (ed.)
1962. *Al'bom indiiskikh i persidskikh miniatyur, XVI–XVIII VV,* Moscow.

Hajek, L.
1960. *Indische Miniaturen vom Hof der Mogulkaiser,* Prague.
Hambly, Gavin
1968. *Cities of Mughal India: Delhi, Agra, and Fatehpur Sikri,* London.
Havell, E.
1928. *Indian Sculpture and Painting,* 2nd edn., London.

Kühnel, Ernst and **Goetz, Hermann**
1926. *Indian Book Painting from Jahangir's Album in the State Library in Berlin,* London.

Maclagan, Sir Edward
1932. *The Jesuits and the Great Mogul,* London.

Martin, F. R.
1912. *The Miniature Painting and Painters of Persia, India and Turkey from the 8th to the 18th century,* London.
Mughal Miniatures
1953. *Mughal Miniatures of the Earlier Periods, Bodleian Picture Books No. 9,* Oxford.

Pinder-Wilson, R. H.
1956. 'A Persian Translation of the Mahābhārata, A Note on the Miniatures', *British Museum Quarterly,* XX, pp. 63–5.
1957. 'Three Illustrated Manuscripts of the Mughal Period', *Ars Orientalis,* II, pp. 413–22.
1969. 'An Illustrated Mughal Manuscript from Ahmadabad', *Paintings from Islamic Lands,* Oxford, pp. 160–71.

Rogers, A.
1909–14. *The Tūzuk-i Jahangīrī, or Memoirs of Jahangir,* London.

Schulz, P. W.
1914. *Die persisch-islamische Miniaturmalerei,* Leipzig.
Skelton, Robert
1957. 'The Mughal artist Farrokh Beg', *Ars Orientalis,* II, pp. 393–411.
1969. 'Two Mughal Lion Hunts', *Victoria and Albert Museum Yearbook,* I, pp. 33–48.
1970. 'Mughal Paintings from Harivamsa Manuscript', *Victoria and Albert Museum Yearbook,* II, pp. 41–54.
1973. 'Early Golconda Painting', *Indolgen-Tagung 1971,* Wiesbaden, pp. 182–95.
1976. 'Indian Painting of the Mughal Period', part V, *The Keir Collection,* ed. B. W. Robinson, London.
Smart, E. S.
1973. 'Four Illustrated Baburnama Manuscripts', *Art and Archaeology Research Papers,* III, London, p. 54.
1974. 'Graphic evidence for Mughal architectural plans', *Art and Archaeology Research Papers,* VI, London, p. 22.
Soustiel, J.
1973. *Miniatures Orientales de l'Inde,* Paris.
1974. Objets d'Art de l'Islam-2,
Stchoukine, Ivan
1929. *La Peinture Indienne à l'époque des Grands Moghols,* Paris.
1931. 'Quelques images de Jahangir dans un divan de Hafiz', *Gazette des Beaux-Arts,* VI, pp. 160–7.
Suleiman, H.
1970. *Miniatures of the Babur-nama,* Tashkent.

Welch, S. C.
1959. 'Early Mughal Miniature paintings from two private collections shown at the Fogg Art Museum', *Ars Orientalis,* III, pp. 133–46.
1961. 'The paintings of Basāwah', *Lalit Kalā,* X, pp. 7–17.
1964. *The Art of Mughal India, Paintings and Precious Objects* (catalogue of an exhibition shown in the galleries of Asia House), New York.
1973. *A Flower from Every Meadow, Indian Paintings from American Collections* (catalogue of exhibition held in Asia House Gallery, 1973), New York.
Wellesz, Emmy
1952. *Akbar's religious thought reflected in Mughal painting,* London.

Wilkinson, J. V. S.
1929. *The Lights of Canopus : Anvār i Suhailī*, London.
1948. *Mughal Painting*, London.
1957. 'An Indian Manuscript of the Golestān of the Shāh Jahān period', *Ars Orientalis*, II, pp. 423–5.